The BIOGENESIS *of* STARCH GRANULES *in* HIGHER PLANTS

The BIOGENESIS *of* STARCH GRANULES *in* HIGHER PLANTS

N. P. BADENHUIZEN
UNIVERSITY OF TORONTO

New York / APPLETON-CENTURY-CROFTS

DIVISION OF MEREDITH CORPORATION

698-1

Library of Congress Card Number: 69-11948

PRINTED IN THE UNITED STATES OF AMERICA

E 04830

PREFACE

Starch is one of our main foods and has innumerable applications in industry. Produced in living plant cells where, in the shape of granules, it is deposited inside certain structures or organelles called plastids, it is of fundamental interest to the biologist.

As biological objects both in shape and fine structure, starch granules show great diversification in plant species. To acquire an insight into the factors that control starch formation, it is necessary to correlate the results of chemical studies with biological data and bring about the integration of structure and function of plastids. The electron microscope has opened new perspectives for such integration.

The material in this book is divided into two parts. Part One presents the problem of starch formation in its general scope and links the experimental results obtained from various starch types. Part Two shows what the specific contribution of each starch has been, and points up the differences which should make us careful in our approach to generalizations. There are frequent cross references. It ought to be noted that many fundamental problems in carbohydrate metabolism have not been touched upon in this book as they can be found elsewhere.

This book is to enable workers in the starch field to become quickly oriented about the background of the biological problems involved. While the subject-matter is still full of controversial problems, the problems concerning starch biogenesis offer excellent illustrations of the complexity of biological phenomena and emphasize the need for experimental attack on all fronts. It would be a rich reward if students are stimulated into original thinking and interest in this fascinating field of study.

N. P. B.

CONTENTS

Part ONE

General Considerations of Starch Biogenesis

A SERIES OF REVIEWS ON VARIOUS FUNDAMENTAL ASPECTS OF STARCH chemistry has recently been published.[1] While reading these surveys, covering such fields as chemistry, biophysics, enzymology, microscopy, and genetics, one is left with the impression that much has been achieved, but also that many gaps still have to be filled in before we can arrive at a comprehensive picture of the starch granule and the factors that influence its development and structure. There are still many discrepancies, notably in the evaluation of the enzymes involved in starch synthesis. Important results have been obtained, but, as happens so often, the differences between the interpretation of laboratory experiments and the actual events taking place in the organelles of the living plant cell, remain considerable. For this reason only a brief review is given of the enzymological background of starch formation.

A source of confusion is found in the many types of starches produced in plants. Not only do species differ in the shapes of their reserve starch granules, but the properties of the starch granules themselves vary considerably. With some experience it is possible to recognize many plants by means of microscopic investigation of their reserve starch, and taxonomic systems have been devised on that basis.[2] This implies that the problem of the structure of the starch granules is fundamentally a genetic one, involving the organelles

[1] R. L. Whistler and E. F. Paschall, ed., *Starch: Chemistry and Technology*, vol. 1 (New York, Academic Press, 1965).

[2] J. B. McNair, *Field Museum Nat. Hist.* (*Bot. Ser.*), **9**, 1 (1930); E. T. Reichert, *Carnegie Inst. Publ.*, **173** (1913); and M. Wellendorf, *Bot. T.*, **59**, 209 (1963).

(plastids) in which they are produced. What part do plastids play in determining the final shape and composition of the starch granule, or are all starch characteristics determined by the cell nucleus? Before answering such a question it is necessary to study the structural and chemical composition of the plastids, especially in relation to nucleic acids.

Most of our present knowledge in this respect has been derived from the study of chloroplasts. This is understandable, since these important plastids contain photosynthetic apparatus and can easily be isolated for *in vitro* studies. The structure of chloroplasts is complicated and consists of a system of pouch-like flat bags or thylakoids which build up a system of grana and intergrana connections (Figs. 6-7 and 6-8); the behavior of chloroplasts in relation to starch production is unique in many respects (p. 100). Unless chloroplasts change their function in aging leaves, they only produce transitory starch in the shape of tiny granules. Although this assimilatory starch will be considered, our main concern here will be with those starch granules which are deposited in reserve organs such as tubers and seeds (reserve starch). The question then remains: what is known about the plastids that evolve reserve starch, the so-called amyloplasts? Apart from some structural details, our knowledge of amyloplasts is scanty indeed when compared to chloroplasts.

Some amyloplasts may also contain chlorophyll[3] and care should be taken to avoid using the term *plastid* as a synonym for *chloroplast.* Because there are as many starch types as there are plant species, it should be specified which starch was investigated before conclusions are drawn from such studies.

Nevertheless, some generalizations are possible and an attempt will be made to discover these on the basis of diversification. To do this we examine what is known about the biogenesis of some starches in a few higher plants. It will then become clear that the study of phenomena such as swelling and degradation processes (amylolytic breakdown, causing corrosion of starch granules) can be valuable in understanding starch granule structure, which, in turn, is dependent upon the way the granule developed in the plastid. A clarification of the biogenesis of the starch granule will provide the key to the structure of the starch granule.

[3] N. P. Badenhuizen, *Rev. Biol.* (*Lisbon*), **4**, 113 (1964).

CHAPTER ONE

THE PLASTIDS

PLASTIDS ARE CYTOPLASMIC ORGANELLES WITH THE ABILITY TO MAKE starch; they are surrounded by an envelope consisting of two membranes (p. 43, see Figs. 1-5 and 1-6). Plastids are characteristic of plant cells, with the exception of bacteria, fungi, and blue-green algae. Sometimes they remain colorless, as in the epidermis of most higher plants, and are then called *leucoplasts.* When they accumulate chlorophyll they are called *chloroplasts* and are found in the green parts of plants. If chloroplasts lose their chlorophyll they become yellow or orange *chromoplasts* containing carotenoids only. All are able at one stage or another to produce starch, but in some cases the final products are oils (p. 98) or proteins (p. 10). *Amyloplasts* are plastids which specialize in the formation of reserve starch granules.

Whatever their structure or pigment content, the *plastids* are the organelles in which the processes of starch biogenesis take place (except in the red algae, where starch granules are formed outside the plastids). Knowledge of the composition and the function of plastids is therefore essential in understanding starch production. In the following pages we investigate the relation between plastids and starch-synthesizing mechanisms.

1-1. PLASTIDS AND STARCH FORMATION

According to Winkler plastids were absent in the white parts of the variegated leaves of *Pandanus veitchii* Hort., a well-known ornamental plant.[1] However, an investigation with the electron microscope by the author disclosed the presence of plastids in those tissues, although they were small and poorly developed, like those in Figure 1-1. Young, undeveloped plastids are often called *proplastids* (Fig.

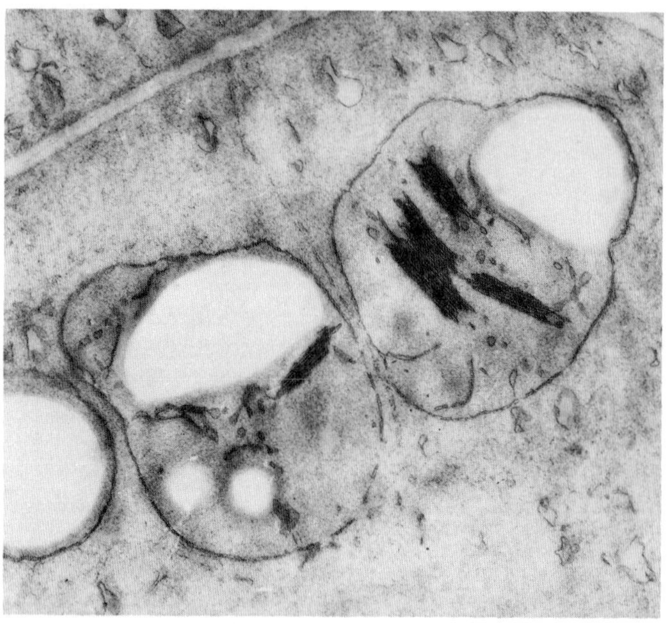

FIG. 1-1. Ultrathin section through plastids in a young cotyledon of soybean. The white patches are starch granules. The stroma contains grana, vesicles, and membrane fragments. Interruptions in the wall of the plastids are artifacts caused by the fixation. $KMnO_4$ fix. Prim. magnif. 4000 ×.

1-2). Proplastids were found in the cells of developing cotyledons of soybeans on the eighteenth day after flowering, although three days before the cells only contained ribosomes and endoplasmic reticulum.[2] This looked like an excellent opportunity to study the origins of plastids (p. 39), but electron pictures of very young stages

[1] H. Winkler, *Jb. wiss. Bot.*, **32**, 525 (1898).
[2] R. F. Bils and R. W. Howell, *Crop Sci.*, **3**, 304 (1963).

always revealed the presence of a few plastids. More recently no plastids could be found in the companion cells of the secondary phloem of the American Basswood;[3] however, they are certainly present in the companion cells of other plants, such as primroses.[4]

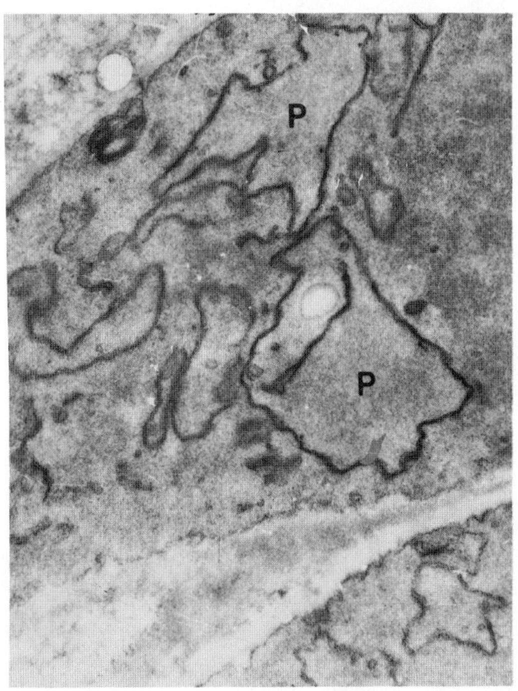

FIG. 1-2. Ultrathin section through proplastids (P) of a very young leaf of *Pellionia*. The highly irregular contour may be a consequence of amoeboid movements of the living proplastid. Glutaraldehyde and Os fix. Prim. magnif. 7000 ×.

Therefore, living cells of higher plants are characterized by the presence of plastids; exceptions are rare, if they exist at all.

The plastids in Figure 1-1 contain small starch granules. Winkler demonstrated long ago that in principle all types of plastids are

[3] R. F. Evert and L. Murmanis, *Amer. J. Bot.*, **52**, 95 (1965).
[4] S. R. Tamulevich and R. F. Evert, *Planta*, **69**, 319 (1966).

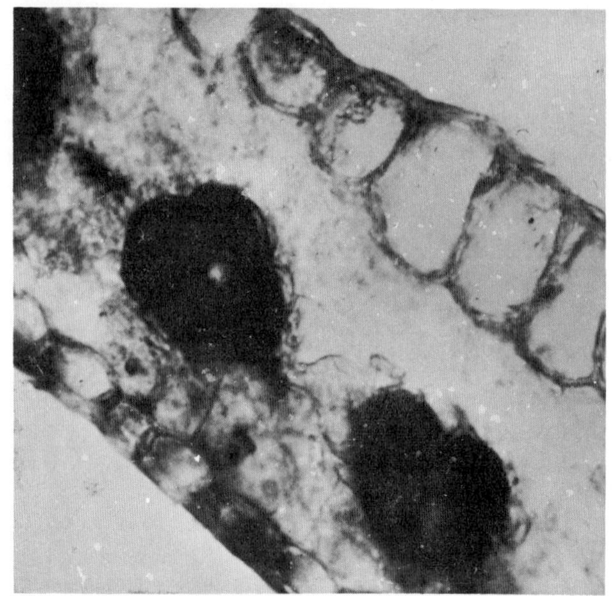

(a)

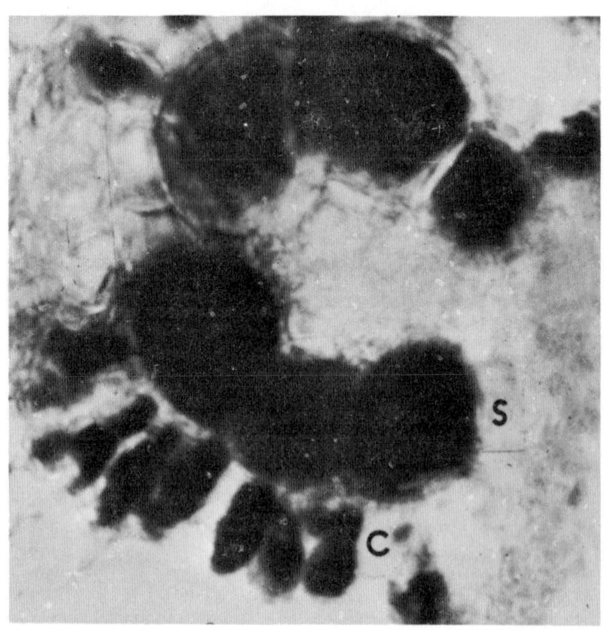

(b)

able to produce starch.[5] In this respect there is no difference between leucoplasts, chloroplasts, and chromoplasts. Even if under natural conditions plastids do not form starch, as, for instance, in the epidermis of many higher plants (excluding the guard cells of the stomata, p. 96) they still can be induced to produce starch if the tissues are floated on a sugar solution. Exceptions to this rule are provided by some Monocotyledons, such as the onion, although even this plant contains some starch in its root tips.[6] Winkler concluded that such plants could not form starch because their starch-precursor content was too low—but perhaps the enzymes involved in starch synthesis are absent or inhibited (p. 11).

An interesting case of inhibition is found in the leaves of corn, sugar cane, and of *Cynodon dactylon* Pers. (Bermuda grass, widely used in South Africa for greens). The leaf anatomy of these grasses is similar: a ring of large, thin-walled cells around the vascular bundle contains unusually large chloroplasts, while the cells of the surrounding chlorenchyma have small chloroplasts. The large chloroplasts of corn[7] or sugar cane without grana,[8] and those of *Cynodon* with grana,[9] contain starch, in contrast to the small chloroplasts[10] [Fig. 1-3(a)]. An increased supply of sugars is sufficient to bring about starch production in the small chloroplasts as well [Fig. 1-3(b)]. It has been suggested that sugars move from the chlorenchyma to the vascular sheath, leaving the former with a deficit and providing the latter with the excess necessary for starch formation.[11]

[5] Winkler, *op. cit.*

[6] Y. Konagamitsu and H. Ono, *Sieboldia,* **2,** 143 (1959).

[7] A. E. Vatter, *Diss. Abstr.,* **16,** 851 (1956).

[8] W. M. Laetsch, D. A. Stetler, and A. J. Vlitos, *Z. Pflanzenphysiol.,* **54,** 472 (1966).

[9] N. P. Badenhuizen and E. N. Lawson, *Amer. J. Bot.,* **49,** 158 (1962).

[10] M. M. Rhoades and A. Carvalho, *Bull. Torrey Bot. Club,* **71,** 335 (1944).

[11] *Ibid.*

FIG. 1-3. (a) Section through a corn leaf. Iodine has stained the vascular sheath cells blue, showing that only those cells produce starch under natural conditions. (b) Section through a leaf of *Cynodon* after incubation with a glucose solution. Both sheath (S) and chlorenchyma (C) cells stain blue with iodine. Incubation with a G–1–P solution, containing $HgCl_2$, would give the same effect.

For an investigation of the starch-synthesizing enzymes in the plastids, two systems may be considered (p. 27). Starch phosphorylase uses glucose-1-phosphate (G–1–P) to build up long chains in which the glucose residues are linked together by α, 1-4 bonds. A primer or starter molecule with the same glucosidic bonds and containing at least three glucose residues, is necessary to allow the reaction to proceed.[12] The chains can then become branched with the establishment of α, 1-6 linkages when Q-enzyme is present.

The second type of enzyme (ADPG-alpha-glucan glucosyl transferase) transfers a glucose unit from adenosine diphosphate glucose (ADPG) to an oligosaccharide or a starch molecule. Attempts to bring about the formation of starch in plastids when ADPG is offered as substrate have been negative so far, but it is easy to demonstrate the presence of phosphorylase in plastids by incubating tissues with a G–1–P solution and staining the starch produced with iodine after several hours of treatment.[13] This applies also to plastids which form noncarbohydrate end products. Thaler described giant plastids in the epidermis cells of *Helleborus corsicus* Willd. and marked them as proteinoplasts.[14] Figure 1-4 shows that these plastids, too, contain phosphorylase, although in some cases a negative result has been reported.[15]

Winkler had not been able to produce starch in the epidermal leucoplasts of orchids and *Commelinaceae* by means of sugar solutions, but the phosphorylase test is positive for these plastids. In fact orchids and *Commelinaceae* offer especially good material for this histochemical reaction.[16] What factors, other than lack of sugar supply, can be responsible for the failure of a plastid to produce starch under natural conditions? (See also p. 93.)

Returning to *Cynodon,* it was found that both large and small chloroplasts show photosynthetic reduction, as demonstrated with the tetrazolium blue test.[17] The test is an indicator for the

[12] M. Abdullah, E. H. Fisher, M. J. Qureshi, K. N. Slessor, and W. J. Whelan, *Biochem. J.,* **97,** 9 P (1965); and D. French and G. M. Wild, *J. Amer. Chem. Soc.,* **75,** 4490 (1953).

[13] H. C. Yin, *Nature,* **162,** 928 (1948).

[14] I. Thaler, *Protoplasma,* **44,** 437 (1955).

[15] G. Heinrich, *Protoplasma,* **61,** 157 (1966).

[16] K. Paech and E. Krech, *Planta,* **41,** 391 (1953).

[17] N. P. Badenhuizen, J. E. Bartlett, and E. N. Gude, *S. Afr. J. Sci.,* **54,** 37 (1958).

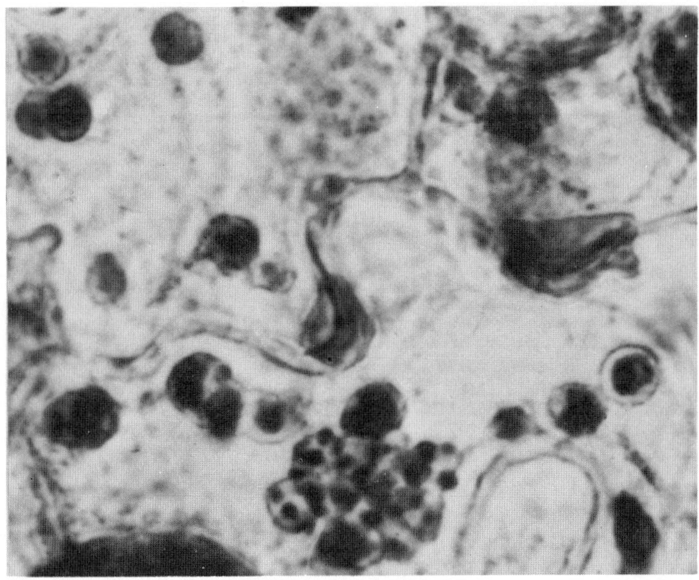

Fig. 1-4. Starch formation in the giant plastids of the epidermis of *Helleborus corsicus* after incubation with 0.5% G–1–P solution for 6 hours. The preparation was stained with iodine.

Hill reaction,[18] so it is reasonable to assume that both types of chloroplasts function normally. Still, the phosphorylase test was positive in the large chloroplasts only, which indicated the presence of a natural inhibitor in the small ones. Several inhibitors of phosphorylase are known, among them phloridzin,[19] iodine, phosphates and other salts,[20] onion juice,[21] and β-amylase.[22] The most likely inhibitor in *Cynodon* chlorenchyma would be amylase, and indeed, if mercuric chloride is added to the G—1—P solution, the phosphorylase test becomes positive also for the small chloroplasts[23] [Fig. 1-3(b)]. Mercuric chloride in a concentration of 2×10^{-4} *M* sup-

[18] M. T. Dyar, *Amer. J. Bot.*, **40,** 20 (1953).
[19] P. Bernfeld and A. Metémédian, *Helv. Chim. Acta,* **31,** 1735 (1948).
[20] H. K. Porter, *Ann. Rev. Plant Physiol.,* **13,** 303 (1962).
[21] M. T. Dyar, *Amer. J. Bot.,* **37,** 786 (1950).
[22] H. K. Porter, *Biochem. J.,* **47,** 476 (1950).
[23] Badenhuizen, Bartlett, and Gude, *op. cit.*

presses amylase activity[24] and although it also partially inhibits phosphorylase,[25] enough of the latter enzyme is left for starch synthesis. Using the same method, phosphorylase was found in the chloroplasts of wheat leaves, which normally do not produce starch.[26] Conversely it has been suggested that the action of starch-hydrolyzing enzymes may be inhibited in all tissues accumulating starch, such as proliferating wound callus.[27] The interference of β-amylase may also be responsible for the existence of two different periods of winter dormancy in grape vine shoots, by preventing starch synthesis at 24°C in December, while the disappearance of amylase during January allowed starch formation to take place at the same optimum temperature.[28]

It may be concluded that plastids in higher plants have the potential to produce starch and that they contain phosphorylase. Both are located in the stroma, the ground substance of the plastid, in which the lipid structures are embedded. Assimilatory starch granules are therefore always formed between thylakoids in the mature chloroplast (see Figs. 6-7 and 6-8).

Before the development of the photosynthetic apparatus proplastids often contain starch granules, and are then considered temporary amyloplasts.

The two unit membranes surrounding the plastids are usually situated closely together (Figs. 1-5 and 1-6; see also Fig. 2-1). In exceptional cases they can separate locally and accumulate stroma in the widening; this newly-formed stroma or neostroma is also able to form starch granules.[29]

Some work has been done on the influence of light on plastid size and starch production. Schumacher[30] observed that when chloroplasts decreased in size after a period of darkness, they produced starch. In fern prothallia, subjected to blue light, the chloroplasts became larger and produced mainly proteins; in red light, a shift took place towards carbohydrate synthesis and the chloroplasts decreased in size.[31]

24 H. K. Porter, *J. Exper. Bot.*, **4**, 44 (1953).
25 H. Ono, *Sieboldia*, **1**, 171 (1956).
26 R. Aimi and T. Murakami, *Proc. Crop. Sci. Soc. Japan*, **23**, 277 (1955).
27 S. Kupila-Ahvenniemi, *Aquilo* (*Ser. Bot.*), **4**, 37 (1966).
28 J. Eifert and A. Eifert, *Nature*, **212**, 1056 (1966).
29 F. Schötz and L. Diers, *Planta*, **69**, 258 (1966).
30 W. Schumacher, *Jb. wiss. Bot.*, **70**, 388 (1929).
31 R. Bergfeld, *Ber. Dt. Bot. Ges.*, **78**, 69 (1965).

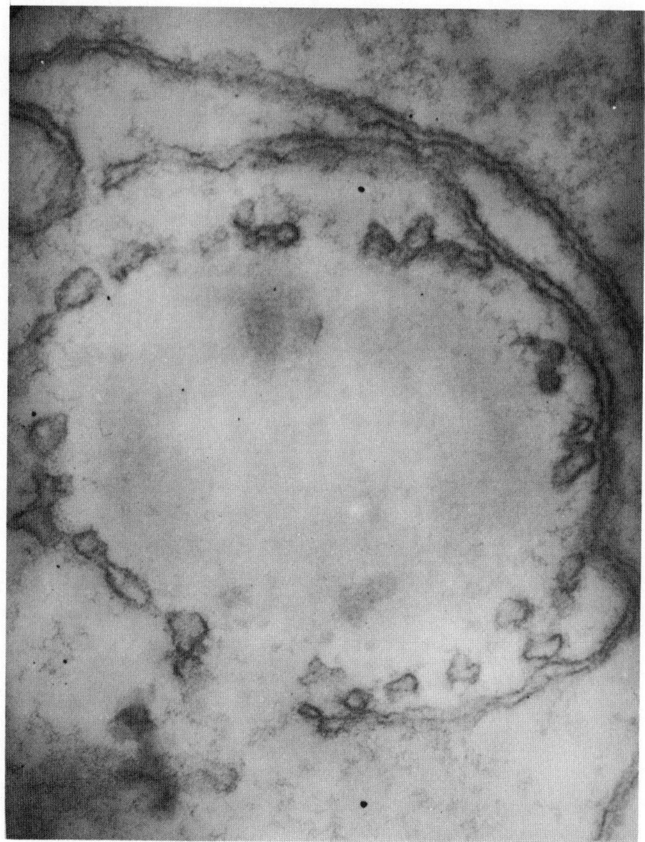

FIG. 1-5. Ultrathin section through an amyloplast in the endosperm of a corn plant, genotype *su₂wx*. Note the "double" membranes. Vesicles in the stroma have become arranged in a circle and some of them are fusing. This ring would have become a double membrane at a later stage. It provides a "pocket," inside which starch is being formed. $KMnO_4$ fix. Prim. magnif. 40,000 ×.

In contrast, brief exposures of etiolated bean leaves to white or red light induced plastid growth and protein and lipid synthesis in the dark; in this initial stage no grana or chlorophyll were formed. The induction of plastid growth could be reversed by subsequent irradiation with wavelengths in the far-red. The antagonism between the effects of far-red and near-red wavelengths is commonly

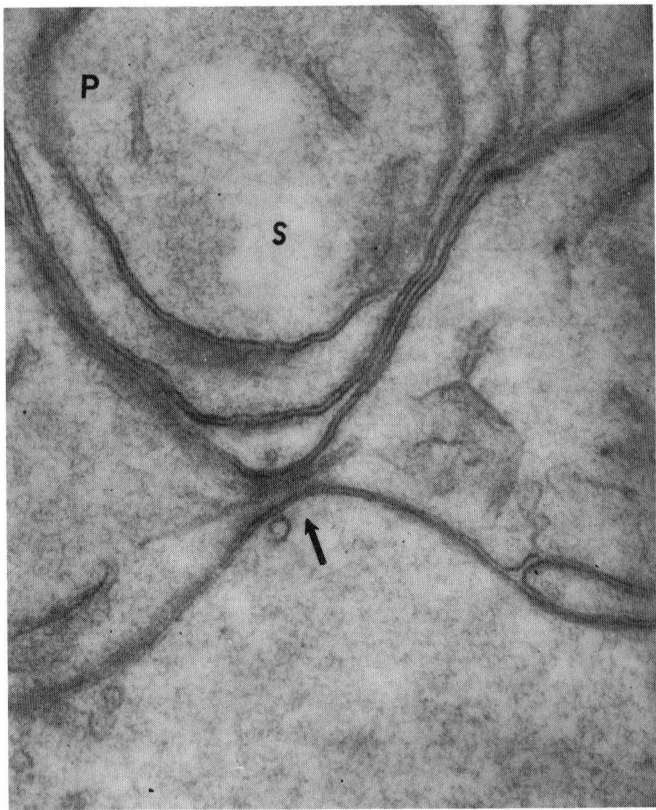

FIG. 1-6. Ultrathin section through part of a dividing plastid in the endosperm of *su2wx* corn. In between the future daughter plastids another plastid (P) fits in near the constriction, which is marked by an arrow. In this plastid, starch (S) is formed within the area limited by three lamellar structures. Note the double membranes. $KMnO_4$ fix. Prim. magnif. 40,000 ×.

taken to be indicative for the presence of a pigment, called *phytochrome,* which occurs in higher plants. Phytochrome is responsible for the regulation of a number of growth processes, although its function is not yet understood completely. The initial stages of plastid growth, then, may be influenced by this phytochrome.[32]

[32] J. R. Mego and A. T. Jagendorf, *Biochim. Biophys. Acta,* **53**, 237 (1961).

Other mechanisms that may be controlled by this pigment were observed in etiolated corn leaves[33] and in a moss:[34] red light promoted starch degradation and far-red counteracted this. The conclusion has been that the starch-synthesizing mechanism in chloroplasts operates in both light and darkness, but that the starch-degrading processes may be activated by phytochrome. It would follow that the pathways for the synthesis and breakdown of starch are different. In prolonged darkness the starch-synthesizing enzymes and other proteins disappear completely from chloroplasts (p. 100). A relationship between plastid size and starch production does not exist.

1-2. PLASTID STRUCTURE IN RELATION TO STARCH FORMATION

The most elaborate structures of plastids are found in the chloroplast, which in the mature stage shows a complicated system of thylakoids, with grana as the main characteristic (see Fig. 6-8). The assimilatory or transitory starch granules are small and embedded in the stroma between the thylakoids. This lamellar system is very stable in the chloroplast and only leaves space for the production of extremely small starch granules; an extra supply of sugars will therefore increase the number of granules, not their size. Because of the close proximity of the thylakoids, these starch granules are often disc-shaped (see Fig. 6-8).

While still in the stage of the proplastid, the organelles possess little or no lamellar structure, and starch granules can form freely in the stroma (the temporary amyloplast stage mentioned above) (see Figs. 1-1 and 1-2). This often leads to the formation of compound starch granules, as happens, for instance, in tobacco leaves when the chloroplast structures degenerate and the space becoming available in the stroma is filled up with starch.[35] This involves a change from chloroplast to *chloroamyloplast;*[36] the starch deposited in the latter is of the reserve type, because its formation is independent of a

33 L. Price, K. Mitrakos, and W. H. Klein, *Quart. Rev. Biol.*, **39**, 11 (1964); and L. Price, K. Mitrakos, and W. H. Klein, *Physiol. Plant.*, **18**, 540 (1965).

34 L. W. Hahn and J. H. Miller, *Physiol. Plant.*, **19**, 134 (1966).

35 N. P. Badenhuizen, *Meded. Proefsta. Vorstenl. Tabak,* **89**, 75 (1941).

36 N. P. Badenhuizen, *Rev. Biol.* (*Lisbon*), **4**, 113 (1964).

photosynthetic apparatus. A similar process takes place when lack of nutrition leads to deficiency symptoms.[37] After the tobacco leaf has become entirely yellow, most of the starch has disappeared again[38]—so a tobacco leaf acts only as a temporary storage organ. Starch granules in leaves never have a definite shape by which they can be recognized. In general: tissues, which are more or less easily destarched in darkness, contain small starch granules that have no characteristic shape.[39]

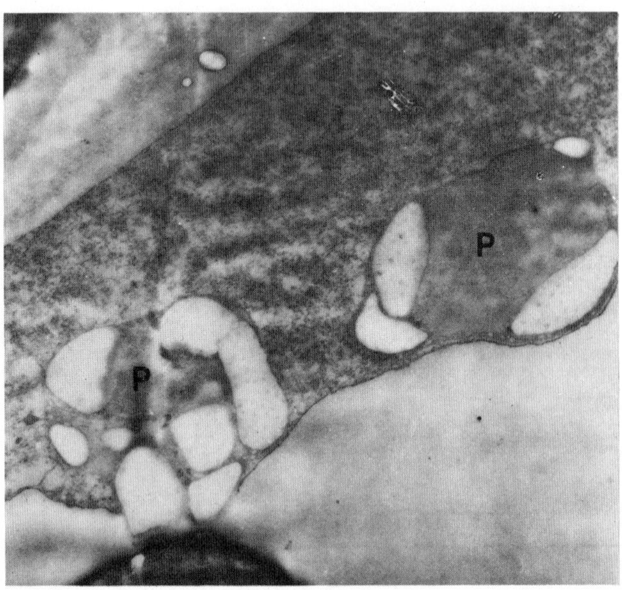

Fig. 1-7. Ultrathin section through two plastids (P) in the nutritive zone of a *Pachypsylla* gall on a leaf of *Celtis*. Several starch granules have been formed at the periphery of the stroma. Glutaraldehyde and Os fix. Prim. magnif. 4000 ×.

Figures 1-7 and 1-8 show stages in the development of compound starch granules in the nutritive tissue of a gall, caused by the hemipteran *Pachypsylla mamma* Riley on the leaves of *Celtis occi-*

[37] F. M. Gerola and G. Dassu, *Caryologia,* **13,** 398 (1960).
[38] N. K. Matheson and J. M. Wheatley, *Austral. J. Biol. Sci.,* **15,** 445 (1962).
[39] Kupila-Ahvenniemi, *op. cit.*

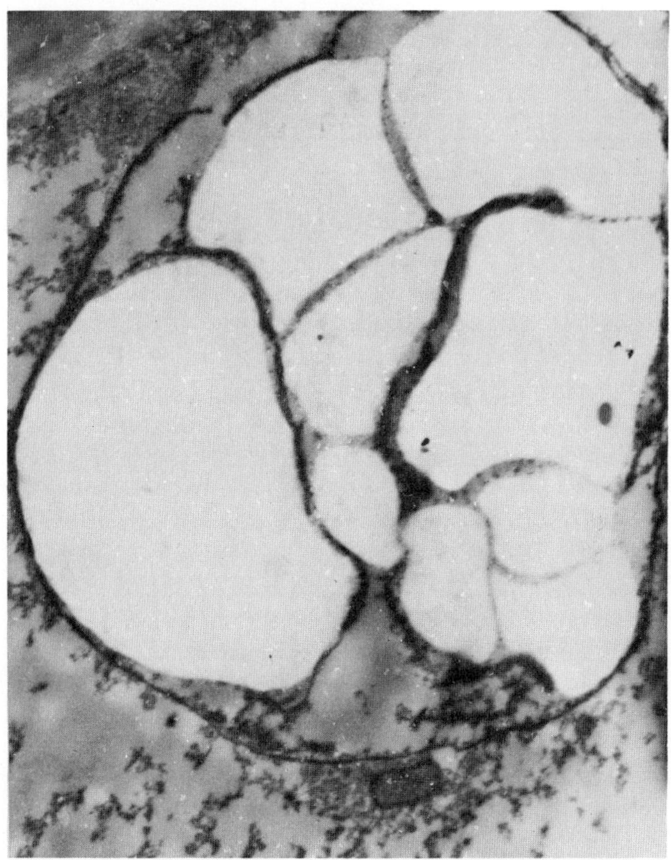

FIG. 1-8. Ultrathin section through a compound starch granule in a plastid of a *Pachypsylla* gall. $KMnO_4$ fix. Prim. magnif. 4000 ×.

dentalis L.[40] Originally, these plastids were chloroplasts, but they lost their structure and formed several starch granules (Fig. 1-7), which then grew together into a compound granule (Fig. 1-8). The parts of the compound granule are still separated by narrow bands of stroma, as in the compound starch granules of rice.[41] The starch granules originate at the periphery of the plastid (Fig. 1-7); gen-

40 T. R. Dundon, *Amer. J. Bot.*, **49**, 800 (1962).
41 M. S. Buttrose, *Naturwiss.*, **49**, 307 (1962).

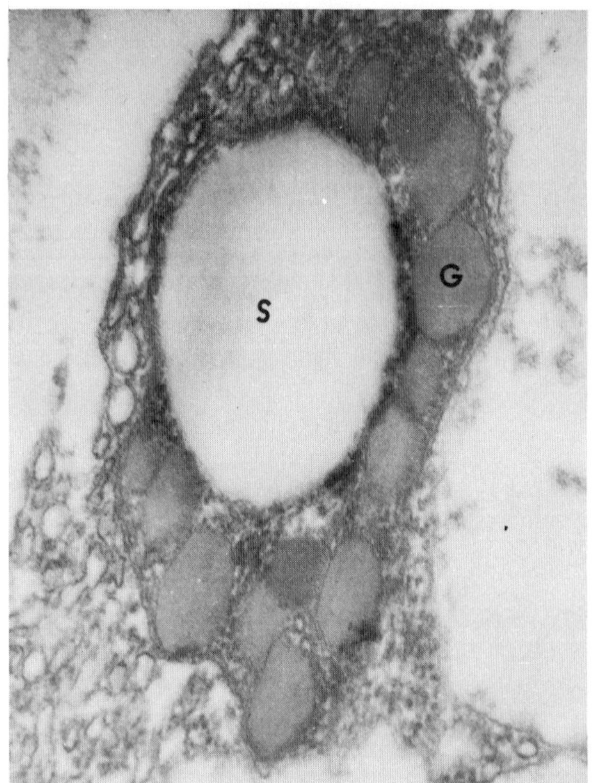

FIG. 1-9. Ultrathin section through a chromoplast from the red part of a flower of *Aloe petricola* Pole Evans. It contains one starch granule (S) which is surrounded by lipid droplets (globules) (G) containing carotenoids. The photosynthetic apparatus has disappeared. Os fix. Prim. magnif. 40,000 ×.

erally they are formed not far from the plastidal envelope (see Fig. 1-13). The development of compound starch granules can also be followed in the guard cells of leaf stomata and, for instance, during the transition of chloroplasts to chromoplasts in many fruits.[42]

Aloe leaves turn red when the African winter period arrives. During this process the chloroplasts are transformed into chromoplasts. They accumulate much starch, while the lamellar structure

[42] M. C. de Rezende-Pinto and R. Salema, *Rev. Biol.* (*Lisbon*), **2**, 51 (1959).

breaks down and is replaced by lipid droplets (globules) containing carotenoids. In the perigone leaves of *Aloe* flowers a similar process takes place;[43] Figure 1-9 shows that the floral chromoplasts are still able to produce starch, although this substance as a rule disappears from the plastids in the reddening leaves.

In reserve organs, like tubers, stems, bulbs, seeds, and so forth, the processes of starch formation do not differ from those in leaf structures; they occur on a broader scale. The starch granules are larger and are stored until such time when new growth requires them as food. An extra supply of sugars will mainly increase the size of the granules, rather than their number. Their shape is characteristic for the plant and genetically controlled.

The central pith of immature potato fruits contains starch granules which are similar to those in the tubers.[44] In the green cortex of the fruit wall pale-green plastids are characteristically grouped around the nucleus (Fig. 1-10), an arrangement seen in many other plants (see Figs. 4-2 and 5-1). These chloroplasts have a poorly developed ultrastructure and in addition, lack of light will

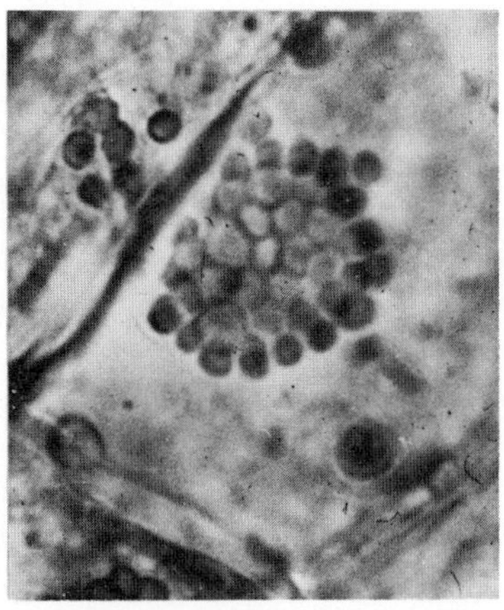

Fig. 1-10. In the living cortex cells of the immature potato berry pale-green plastids are grouped around the nucleus. *cf.* Fig. 6-3.

[43] K. Steffen and F. Walter, *Planta,* **50,** 640 (1958).
[44] C. T. Greenwood and S. MacKenzie, *Stärke,* **15,** 251 (1963).

prevent photosynthesis inside the tissue. As a result the plastids become chloroamyloplasts, which are dependent upon an extra-cellular sugar supply for starch formation. The starch granules formed are compound (*cf.* p. 15) and larger in deeper layers of the cortex (see Fig. 6-3). As in the stem of *Pellionia* (p. 91) the plastids in the peripheral part of the cortex do not produce starch under natural conditions; they contain structures that have been called "intraplastid bodies"[45] and which are similar in appearance to the "pockets" described for *Pellionia* (p. 93).

The difference between these chloroamyloplasts and those in leaves is that no change in function is involved. However, the "permanent" chloroamyloplasts in the cortex of the potato fruit and in the stems of *Pellionia* or *Dieffenbachia* are able to photosynthesize if exposed to light; they contain chlorophyll a and b in normal proportions, and their structure does not differ in principle from that of ordinary chloroplasts. Yet they do not form assimilatory starch, but they grow reserve starch granules from amylogenic or starch-forming "pockets," in which the starch crystallizes out from accumulated starch precursors.[46] The chloroamyloplasts retain their structures for a long time but gradually the lamellae are pushed away, first by the amylogenic pocket, then by the growing starch granule, until they finally disappear (Figs. 1-11 and 1-12.)

At this stage the interesting structure of the *Pellionia* leaf should be noted. Here we can study the two types of plastids side by side in one organ. The green center part consists of two layers which can be easily cut apart, one containing normal chloroplasts, and one with chloroamyloplasts. Characteristically, after leaves have been exposed to continuous light for forty-eight hours, the reserve starch granules increase considerably in size, the assimilatory granules increase only in number.[47]

However, chloroamyloplasts are the exception, rather than the rule, and in general reserve starch granules are produced in *leucoamyloplasts.* These colorless plastids contain little or no membranous structures. If membranous structures are present, they consist of small vesicles and occasionally small lamellar formations situated at

[45] N. G. Marinos, *J. Ultrastruct. Res.,* **17,** 91 (1967).

[46] N. P. Badenhuizen, *Stärke,* **15,** 237 (1963); and R. Salema and N. P. Badenhuizen, *J. Ultrastruct. Res.,* **20,** 383 (1967).

[47] E. Weier, *Cytologia,* **7,** 504 (1936).

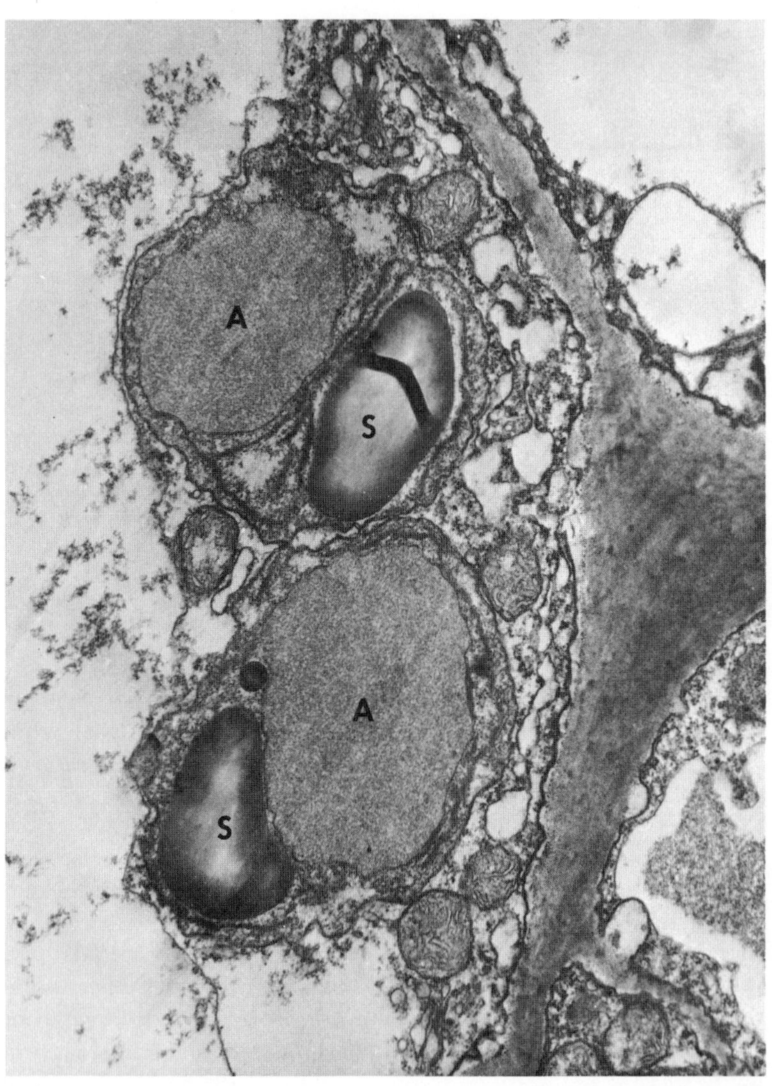

FIG. 1-11. Ultrathin section through two chloroamyloplasts in a very young leaf of *Pellionia*. Each contains an amylogenic pocket (A) surrounded by membrane structures and filled with dense granular matter; a starch granule (S) is next to it. Residues of the thylakoid system are visible in the stroma. Ryter-Kellenberger fix. Prim. magnif. 5000 ×. Photo: R. SALEMA.

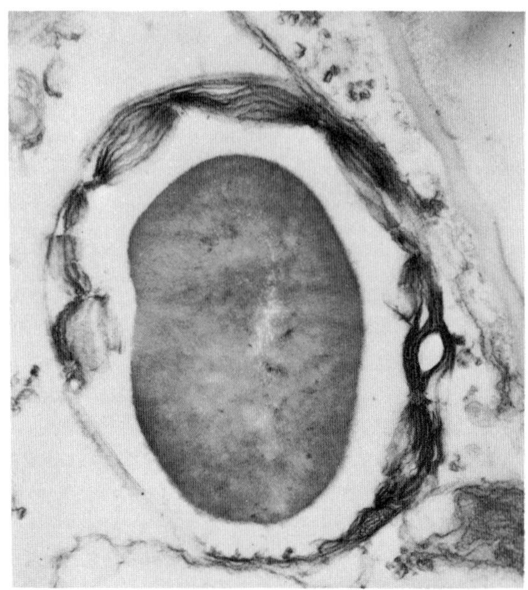

FIG. 1-12. Ultrathin section through a chloroamyloplast from a very young pea cotyledon. A starch granule has been formed and the thylakoid system with grana is situated at the periphery of the stroma. Os fix. Prim. magnif. 8000 ×.

random (Fig. 1-13). Starch granules are formed somewhere in the stroma, or in the enclosure formed by lamellar structures or vesicles, if present (see Figs. 1-1, 1-2, 1-5, 1-6, and 5-2).[48] Such pockets presumably contain a greater concentration of enzymes and their substrates than elsewhere in the stroma. Since diffusion of the materials from the pockets into the stroma would be difficult, the chances are that they will be suitable spots for starch formation. In amyloplasts the structures that constitute a pocket are temporary and will disappear as the plastid matures; in chloroplasts the pockets are permanent and limit the growth of the starch granule (see Fig. 6-8).

In some cases amyloplasts will become green if exposed to light (for instance, potato tubers, *Iris* rhizome, roots of various plants). We do not know why some leucoplasts have this capacity and others do not, but in potato the degree of virescence appears to be geneti-

[48] N. P. Badenhuizen, *Proc. Kon. Nederl. Akad. Wetensch.*, **65** C, 123 (1962).

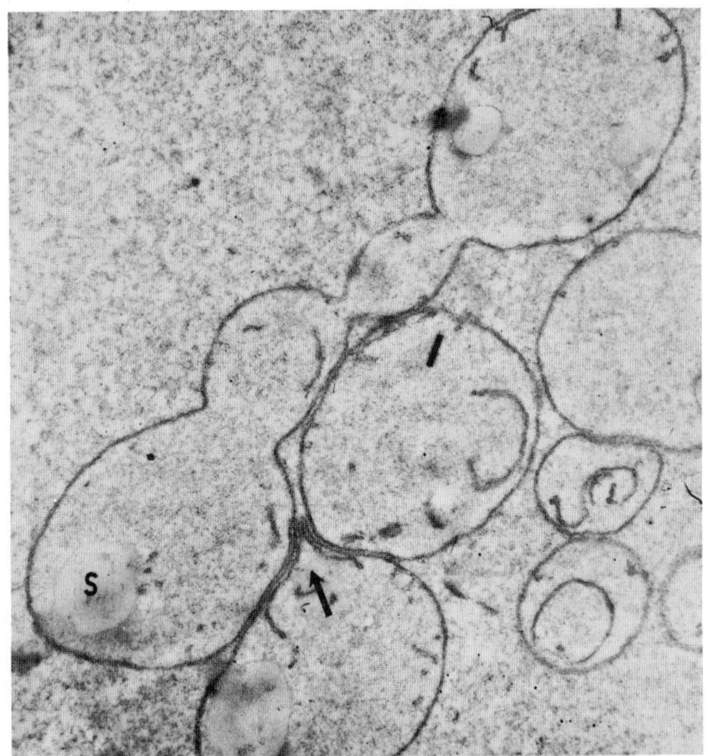

FIG. 1-13. Ultrathin section through plastids from corn endosperm. The plastids are flexible (see arrow). Some show incomplete division —the daughter plastids do not separate and remain small. Starch granules (S) have been formed here and there in the stroma, which contains sparse and random lipid structures. $KMnO_4$ fix. Prim. magnif. 6000 ×.

cally controlled.[49] The stroma of the amyloplasts produces a more or less extensively developed lamellar structure (see Fig. 6-2).

The proplastid often shows an irregular shape under the electron microscope (see Fig. 1-2) and this has been attributed to amoeboid movements of the living organelle.[50]

[49] R. V. Akeley, G. V. C. Houghland, and A. E. Schark, *Amer. Potato J.*, **39**, 409 (1962).

[50] S. Strugger, *Protoplasma,* **43,** 120 (1954); and D. von Wettstein, *Exper. Cell Res.*, **12,** 427 (1957).

The stroma or ground substance of plastids contains proteins and looks homogeneous when viewed with the electron microscope. Starch precursors are formed in the stroma. The difference in the concentration of these substances determines where starch will be produced. The sugar molecules from which starch precursors originate have to pass through the double membrane surrounding the plastid; the same applies to amino acids. It is known that substances pass through the plastidal envelope[51]; vectorial enzymes may be present in the membranes that direct the flow of such substances[52] or the membrane itself may have an asymmetrical structure. Some protein synthesis in chloroplasts is directed by the nucleic acids in these organelles[53] and this system, which is independent of that directed by the nucleus, is responsible for a number of enzymes which are involved in photosynthesis.[54] Nucleic acids (DNA and RNA) are also present in colorless amyloplasts,[55] and will contribute to the proteins in the stroma. The stroma of chloroplasts contains many ribosomes (the sites of protein synthesis) (see Fig. 6-7), that of chloroamyloplasts relatively few (see Fig. 2-2).

In this stroma reserve starch granules with a definite, genetically controlled shape and structure, crystallize. The purified starches do not differ chemically, and the basic reactions which produce the starch molecules can be expected to be the same in all plants. However, there are substances in the stroma that help to determine how starch granules are built up. These substances are both inorganic and organic, such as fatty substances, phosphates and other ions, sugars, oligosaccharides of the maltose series, phosphorylated sugars, nucleotides, amino acids, and proteins—they all are able to influence starch synthesis in one way or other. By binding water to their surface, some of the molecules may also control the amount of water available for hydration of the starch molecules and so influence the crystalline pattern (see p. 51).[56]

If the complex mixture of the stroma is responsible for the production of a certain type of starch granule, this mixture itself must

[51] For supporting literature see Schötz and Diers, *op. cit.*

[52] A. L. Lehninger, *Naturwiss.*, **53**, 57 (1966).

[53] J. Brachet, *Nature*, **213**, 650 (1967).

[54] R. M. Smillie, D. Graham, M. R. Dwyer, A. Grieve, and N. F. Tobin, *Biochem. Biophys. Res. Commun.*, **28**, 604 (1967).

[55] R. Salema and N. P. Badenhuizen, unpublished.

[56] N. P. Badenhuizen, *Nature*, **197**, 464 (1963).

have a fixed composition characteristic for the plant. The crystallization of the starch molecules into a granule is a purely physical process, controlled entirely by the many substances in the stroma. The shape of the starch granule is a reflection of the composition of its environment. The question is then how a characteristic stroma composition is genetically controlled.

First, the basic mechanism of starch formation and how it may be influenced by various factors is considered.

CHAPTER TWO

STARCH-SYNTHESIZING ENZYMES

PHOSPHORYLASE WAS FOUND TO BE CONNECTED WITH THE SITES OF starch synthesis in rice,[1] the tapioca plant,[2] peas,[3] sweet potato,[4] and other plants. In the onion plant, for instance, starch is produced in the root tips—and only there can phosphorylase activity be demonstrated.[5] In contrast, tubers of *Dahlia*[6] or Jerusalem artichokes do not contain the enzyme, and instead of starch the polyfructosan inulin is stored. Since both phosphorylase and starch granules are found in plastids (p. 10), it is difficult to understand why phosphorylase has not retained its place in the literature as a major starch-synthesizing enzyme. Its action is reversible, and the equilibrium:

$$\text{starch} + \text{phosphate (Pi)} \rightleftarrows \text{glucose–1–phosphate (G–1–P)}$$

is pH-dependent.[7] It follows that the ratio Pi/G–1–P is important —a ratio higher than the equilibrium constant favors starch breakdown at any pH. Very high ratios were found during periods of starch accumulation in the locust tree[8] and in rice kernels.[9] The pH in yeast cells is 6.2, and at that pH the equilibrium constant K for the ratio Pi/G–1–P should be 6.3, but again much higher values

1 R. Aimi and T. Murakami, *Proc. Crop. Sci. Soc. Japan,* **23,** 277 (1955).

2 L. M. Srivastava and P. S. Krishnan, *Enzymologia,* **23,** 270 (1961); and P. N. Viswanathan and L. M. Srivastawa, *Indian J. Biochem.,* **1,** 133 (1964).

3 D. H. Turner and J. F. Turner, *Austral. J. Biol. Sci.,* **10,** 302 (1957).

4 R. Aimi, *Proc. Crop. Sci. Soc. Japan,* **24,** 201 (1956).

5 Y. Konagamitsu and H. Ono, *Sieboldia,* **2,** 143 (1959).

6 Viswanathan and Srivastawa, *op. cit.*

7 C. S. Hanes and E. J. Maskell, *Biochem. J.,* **36,** 76 (1942).

8 M. H. Ewart, D. Siminovitch, and D. R. Briggs, *Plant Physiol.,* **29,** 407 (1954).

9 R. Aimi and S. Konno, *Proc. Crop. Sci. Soc. Japan,* **26,** 228 (1958).

were found.[10] In developing peas the ratio decreased from 13 to 2 some days before the rate of starch synthesis increased to a maximum.[11] From such observations the conclusion has been drawn that phosphorylase is not involved in the synthesis, but only in the degradation of starch. However, the ratio Pi/G–1–P is dependent on many factors, and its overall value for whole cells may not have the significance often attached to it.

There is little doubt that phosphorolysis plays a role in starch degradation, together with amylolysis by amylases and debranching enzymes,[12] although to evaluate the relative importance of phosphorylase and amylases if both types of enzymes are present is as yet impossible. To assess the function of phosphorylase as a starch-synthesizing enzyme we must know the conditions prevailing in its immediate environment in the cell. As Turner and Turner put it: "Results of gross analysis of tissues may bear little relation to the actual concentration of reactants at the site of synthesis within the cell."[13] An overall high ratio may have several causes: (1) our inability to measure the equilibrium constant at the site of phosphorylase activity; (2) side-tracking of G–1–P into the glycolytic chain; and (3) accumulation of phosphate. If there were a phosphate gradient in the yeast cell, the amount of phosphate at the site of phosphorylase activity might well be low enough to provide for a ratio favoring glucan synthesis.[14]

Using Tandler's method for the detection of free phosphate[15] we could demonstrate phosphates in the vacuoles of corn or *Cynodon* mesophyll cells, but not in the chloroplasts. Plastids in higher plants may therefore have a low ratio of Pi/G–1–P. If the pH in plastids ranges from 5 to 6, as was found for the chloroplasts of stomatal cells,[16] the conditions will be right for starch synthesis by means of phosphorylase (*cf*. p. 76).

There may be regions of high G–1–P concentration at the sites

[10] W. E. Trevelyan, P. F. E. Mann, and J. S. Harrison, *Arch. Biochem. Biophys.*, **50**, 81 (1954).

[11] K. S. Rowan and D. H. Turner, *Austral. J. Biol. Sci.*, **10**, 414 (1957).

[12] R. R. Swain and E. E. Dekker, *Biochim. Biophys. Acta*, **122**, 87 (1966).

[13] Turner and Turner, *op. cit.*

[14] Trevelyan, Mann, and Harrison, *op. cit.*

[15] C. J. Tandler, *J. Histochem. Cytochem.*, **5**, 489 (1957).

[16] J. Small, *Protoplasmalogia*, **2**. B 2 C, (1955).

of starch synthesis within the cell. The large chloroplasts of *Cynodon* and corn, for instance, contain organic phosphates, but such phosphates could not be found in the small chloroplasts. These small chloroplasts do not produce starch (p. 9), not only because they contain phosphorylase-inhibiting amylases (p. 11), but also because they have insufficient G–1–P; in addition the chlorenchyma cells contain many more inorganic phosphates than the sheath cells. In other words: the ratio Pi/G–1–P is favorable for starch synthesis in the sheath chloroplasts, but unfavorable in those of the chlorenchyma. No evidence is available that would justify the rejection of phosphorylase as a starch-synthesizing enzyme. It is still, in fact, the only enzyme able to produce starch *in vitro* from a simple substrate, consisting of glucose–1–phosphate and oligosaccharides of the maltose series as primers, starting with maltotriose.

Nevertheless recent reviews recommend the total rejection of phosphorylase as a starch-synthesizing agent, since "there now can be very little doubt that the synthesis of amylose, amylopectin, and phytoglycogen all proceed from nucleoside diphosphate glucose intermediates."[17] The intermediate adenosine diphosphate glucose (ADPG) occurs naturally in plants and reacts faster with the glucosyl transferase enzyme (p. 10) than the uridine compound (UDPG).[18] ADPG-glucosyl transferase has been found in amylose-containing starch granules,[19] in plant juices,[20] and in chloroplasts,[21] be it not in all.[22] It can produce oligosaccharides from maltose and triose and is also able to incorporate glucose into starch granules.[23] It does not occur in waxy corn starch[24] or glutinous rice starch,[25] although it may be present in the supernatant from the endosperm tissues. As

[17] J. H. Nordin and S. Kirkwood, *Ann. Rev. Plant Physiol.,* **16,** 393 (1965).

[18] T. Murata, T. Sugiyama, and T. Akazawa, *Arch. Biochem. Biophys.,* **107,** 92 (1964).

[19] M. A. Rongine de Fekete, L. F. Leloir, and C. E. Cardini, *Nature,* **187,** 918 (1960).

[20] R. B. Frydman, B. C. De Souza, and C. E. Cardini, *Biochim. Biophys. Acta,* **113,** 620 (1966).

[21] A. Doi, K. Doi, and Z. Nikuni, *Biochim. Biophys. Acta,* **113,** 312 (1966).

[22] Viswanathan and Srivastawa, *op. cit.*

[23] L. F. Leloir, M. A. Rongine de Fekete, and C. E. Cardini, *J. Biol. Chem.,* **236,** 636 (1961).

[24] O. E. Nelson and C. Y. Tsai, *Science,* **145,** 1194 (1964).

[25] T. Murata, T. Sugiyama, and T. Akazawa, *Biochem. Biophys. Res. Commun.,* **18,** 371 (1965).

mentioned before, plastids do not produce starch when incubated with ADPG.

Four characteristic features of the ADPG-glucosyl transferase emerge from the literature: (1) oligosaccharides are not able to act as primers for starch synthesis, as was also found to be the case for glycogen formation in rat liver;[26] (2) starting with maltose, alpha-glucan chains of any length can become extended by the addition of a glucose residue, and there the reaction stops; (3) the enzyme has something to do with amylose formation; and (4) the transferase is strongly absorbed to starch molecules.

In the light of these data it is surprising that glucose incorporation into starch is generally equated with starch synthesis *de novo.* This is only possible if one assumes that the lengthening of the chains is a continuous process. However, all experiments indicate that the chain-extending capacity of the glucosyl transferase is limited. When, for instance, the concentration of amylopectin as glucose acceptor from ADPG is kept low, the available free branches quickly become occupied with glucose residues and the rate of ADP formation decreases sharply. At higher amylopectin concentrations there will eventually be a sufficient number of free branches to accept the glucose offered by the ADPG, and ADP production continues until all ADPG has been used.[27] In another experiment the structure of potato starch granules had been loosened in several ways (p. 37); more end groups had become available and as a consequence a higher glucosyl transferase activity was registered in the starch residues. When Q-enzyme was added to such residues, the number of end groups increased again because of the branching action of this enzyme, causing a still higher level of activity as measured by the incorporation of glucose into the starch.[28]

Indeed, for the production of starch *in vitro,* phosphorylase is used—the reason being that this method is more convenient.[29] In reality there is no other method at present. In addition we should remember that the pH of stomatal plastids is 5 to 6 (p. 28), at which pH ADPG-glucosyl transferase is inactive, since its optimum pH

[26] O. G. R. Gödeken, R. Sandrus, and J. M. Olavarria, *Biochim. Biophys. Acta,* **117,** 255 (1966).

[27] Doi, Doi, and Nikuni, *op. cit.*

[28] R. B. Frydman and C. E. Cardini, *J. Biol. Chem.,* **242,** 312 (1967).

[29] J. Mordoh, L. F. Leloir, and C. R. Krisman, *Proc. Nat. Acad. U. S.,* **53,** 86 (1965).

ranges from 7.5 to 8.2.[30] It is most unlikely that such high alkalinities would exist in amyloplasts.

Serious doubts about the importance of ADPG-glucosyl transferase as a starch synthesizing enzyme are therefore justified and have been expressed,[31] while some investigators at least hinted at the possibility that additional enzymes might be involved as well.[32] The question of how starch is formed in the first instance, has not been answered as yet by experiments with ADPG-glucosyl transferase.

A similar problem exists with regard to glycogen synthesis.[33] UDPG-glycogen glucosyl transferase lengthens the free branches of the glycogen molecule by the transfer of glucose to their ends, and it is supposed that the lengthened chains can then become further branched by the action of a branching enzyme.[34] In the absence of primer glycogen the enzyme can not produce glycogen from UDPG, and although maltose is an acceptor of the glucose, it is not a primer for glycogen synthesis. Since the role of phosphorylase in the production of glycogen meets with several controversies, the question of how the first glycogen molecules appeared in the cell has been left unanswered.

One important function of the ADPG-alpha glucan glycosyl transferase might be the production of oligosaccharides from maltose, which then could act as primers for phosphorylase.

Recent investigations of starch formation in potato tubers and corn endosperm[35] tend to confirm the role assigned in this chapter to phosphorylase as the principal starch-synthesizing enzyme. In corn endosperm several phosphorylases were found, one of which seems to be associated with starch synthesis.[36] Much still has to be learned about the exact function of these isozymes, but it is obvious that the evidence, both in the older and the more recent literature, is in favor of starch synthesis by means of phosphorylase.

A tentative scheme of the reactions involved in starch synthesis and degredation is given on p. 112 (Fig. 7-1).

30 P. N. Viswanathan and P. S. Krishnan, *Indian J. Biochem.*, **2**, 16 (1965).

31 N. P. Badenhuizen, *Nature*, **197**, 464 (1963).

32 Doi, Doi, and Nikuni, *op. cit.*

33 P. W. Robbins, A. Wright, and M. Dankert, *J. Gen. Physiol.*, **49**, 331 (1966).

34 B. Illingworth-Brown and D. H. Brown, *Proc. Nat. Acad. U. S.*, **56**, 725 (1966).

35 R. B. Frydman and C. E. Cardini, *Plant Physiol.*, **42**, 628 (1967); and C. Y. Tsai and O. E. Nelson, *Plant Physiol.*, **43**, 103 (1968).

36 Tsai and Nelson, *ibid.*

2-1. THE PRODUCTION OF AMYLOSE AND AMYLOPECTIN

Whatever the ratio between starch phosphorylase or P-enzyme and the branching or Q-enzyme (the ratio P/Q), the final product *in vitro* is always branched.[37] Both enzymes are soluble and are present in the plastidal stroma, where they would be expected to produce amylopectin only. In reality most starches contain amylose chains, which are linear, although they may have a few scattered branching points.[38] The branching points are established through α-1,6 glucosidic linkages, and the enzyme that produces them in amylopectin is Q-enzyme. Both P- and Q-enzymes occur in tissues with starches of varying amylose content, including the waxy and high-amylose varieties. What, then, is the mechanism which prevents a certain genetically fixed number of linear molecules from becoming branched? Several systems have been proposed, but at this stage it is difficult to make a choice. Some systems, however, are supported by experimental evidence more than others.

One possibility is that amylose and amylopectin are produced by two different pathways. It has been suggested that P- and Q-enzymes would produce amylopectin, and that included ADPG-glucosyl transferase would later form amylose inside the starch granule.[39] Such a scheme offers an explanation for the increase in amylose content during the development of the starch granule, or the origin of the so-called "blue cores" in starch granules of waxy cereals (p. 62).[40] On the other hand ADPG-glucosyl transferase is unable to make amylose *in vitro,* a great deal of amylose is already present in the earliest stages of the development of the starch granule, and it is unlikely that there would be room for new, long amylose molecules, once the amylopectin has crystallized out. Since ^{14}C-glucose from labeled ADPG is incorporated into amylose as well as amylopectin,[41] it is difficult to see how a transferase, bringing this

37 P. Bernfeld and A. Meutémédian, *Helv. Chim. Acta,* **31,** 1735 (1948).

38 W. Banks and C. T. Greenwood, *Arch. Biochem. Biophys.,* **117,** 674 (1966); and O. Kjölberg and D. J. Manners, *Biochem. J.,* **84,** 50 P (1962).

39 W. J. Whelan, *Stärke,* **15,** 247 (1963).

40 N. P. Badenhuizen, *Cereal Chem.* **32,** 286 (1955).

41 E. Recondo and L. F. Leloir, *Biochem. Biophys. Res. Commun.,* **6,** 85 (1961).

about by elongation of the amylose chains and the free branches of the amylopectin, could have participated by this activity in the production of linear chains: they have to be there in the first place.

It may be inferred that the measurement of the activity of ADPG-glucosyl transferase by means of glucose incorporation does not give us an insight into the mechanism of amylose production; this equally applies to a joint action of phosphorylase and Q-enzyme in a single two-stage process.[42] Only if P- and Q-enzyme were spatially separated (for which there is no evidence), or if some of the linear molecules were made inaccessible as substrate to the action of Q-enzyme, would amylose be formed.

Not only the presence of amylose, but also the fact that its quantity is genetically controlled, has to be explained. What the relative importance is of the nucleic acids of nucleus and amyloplasts is still an open question. Since the function of the hereditary material is the production of specific proteins, it is reasonable to assume that proteins are involved in shaping the starch granule. If the enzymatic activity of proteins in itself is insufficient to provide an explanation for the existence of amylose, then other properties of these proteins have to be considered.

In this connection two characteristics of ADPG-glucosyl transferase are of special interest: (1) the transferase only occurs in amylose-containing starches, and (2) the transferase is strongly adsorbed to starch molecules. It has therefore been proposed that this protein, by its strong affinity to alpha-glucan chains, may block amylose molecules and prevent them from being branched.[43]

The simplest way to demonstrate that such a process occurs is to show that a direct proportionality exists between amylose content and ADPG-glucosyl transferase activity. Such a relationship was indeed found in the developing starch granules of high amylose corn, where both amylose content and transferase activity increased simultaneously in the endosperm tissue of plants growing under the same conditions. It was also shown that wrinkled pea starch with 66 percent amylose had much more ADPG-glucosyl transferase activity than normal pea starch with 35 percent amylose (see p. 99).[44] The

[42] N. P. Badenhuizen, *Recent Advances in Botany,* **2,** 1258 (Toronto, Univ. Press, 1961).

[43] N. P. Badenhuizen and K. R. Chandorkar, *Cereal Chem.,* **42,** 44 (1965).

[44] K. R. Chandorkar and N. P. Badenhuizen, *Cereal Chem.,* **44,** 27 (1967).

activity is the only measure available of the amount of glucosyl transferase present, but unfortunately it is influenced by factors such as temperature and the nature and age of the plant (see p. 99). If one grows small potato tubers on stem pieces under sterile conditions at high temperature (30°C) little or no transferase activity is found, while the starch has a normal amylose content.[45] The loss of activity does not mean that the protein has disappeared; it still could have exerted a protective function.

For these reasons no correlation is found as a rule if different plants are compared. Moreover, many more protein molecules may be present than would be necessary to block a certain number of amylose molecules (see below), and therefore total activity may not bear an exact relationship to the amount of protein actually adsorbed to the carbohydrate.

Interestingly enough, recent experiments tend to show that ADPG-glucosyl transferase is adsorbed to, and even stabilized by, amylose.[46] Only amylose or amylose-containing starches adsorbed the transferase enzyme from its solution. This would agree with the suggestion that amylose molecules are blocked by the transferase protein,[47] if one could only understand how protein molecules are able to penetrate into starch granules. It has been demonstrated that potato starch granules are inaccessible for such large molecules.[48] There is some evidence that under certain conditions proteins can become adsorbed to the surface of the granules.[49] Could the surface be changed by the presence of amylose in such a way that this adsorption is facilitated? More knowledge of the properties of protein-carbohydrate complexes is required before the preferential adsorption of ADPG-starch glucosyl transferase to amylose, as reported, can be understood. The enzyme can be adsorbed to waxy starch granules by simultaneous precipitation with ammonium sulfate.[50] Evidently the results can vary with the conditions of the experiment (*cf.* also p. 90).

Several investigations have shown that proteins, such as amy-

45 Badenhuizen and Chandorkar, *op. cit.*

46 T. Akazawa and T. Murata, *Biochem. Biophys. Res. Commun.*, **19**, 21 (1965).

47 Badenhuizen and Chandorkar, *op. cit.*

48 G. H. Lathe and C. R. J. Ruthven, *Biochem. J.*, **62**, 665 (1956).

49 K. R. Chandorkar and N. P. Badenhuizen, *Stärke,* **18**, 91 (1966).

50 *Ibid.*

lases, can become adsorbed to starch granules.[51] It was therefore possible that ADPG-glucosyl transferase could be adsorbed to the surface of the granules during their isolation. However, attempts to dislodge the enzyme from such a film by means of elution, detergents, or proteinases gave negative results.[52] This was confirmed in our laboratories, and it was also found that inert potato starch did not take up any demonstrable activity from a solution containing glucosyl transferase.

It is more likely that enzymes become included during the growth of the starch granule. Growth by apposition was established by allowing potato plants to photosynthesize in an atmosphere containing $^{14}CO_2$, and demonstrating that only the peripheral layers of the tuber starch granules became radioactive.[53] Electron pictures of developing starch granules in various plants (p. 65) tend to show that apposition takes place by the addition of particles to the surface (Figs. 2-1 and 2-2).[54] If these particles are coacervate droplets in which alpha-glucan chains are formed, then they are the sites of enzyme action. While they are incorporated into the granule surface they trap proteins, which by their inclusion become an integral part of the starch granule (p. 37).

Starch granules appear to contain various metabolic intermediates[55] and the mechanism to use these for the elongation of existing chains under the influence of various enzymes.[56] Such endogenous activity, resulting in intussusception, might be one of the factors that cause an apparent increase in linear material during the development of starch granules (p. 68).

Phosphorylase is not included in the granule, but it can be adsorbed to the surface, or the enzyme is free in the stroma, depending upon locally prevailing conditions (p. 107). Its main action is therefore in the stroma, whereas ADPG-glucosyl transferase is found both in the stroma and inside the starch granule. If phosphorylase is considered to be the enzyme that can produce starch

[51] See literature in Chandorkar and Badenhuizen, *Stärke, ibid.;* see also Viswanathan and Srivastawa, *op. cit.*

[52] Frydman and Cardini, *op. cit.*

[53] N. P. Badenhuizen and R. W. Dutton, *Protoplasma,* **47,** 156 (1956).

[54] N. P. Badenhuizen, *Proc. Kon. Nederl. Akad. Wetensch.,* **65** C, 123 (1962).

[55] H. J. Duncan and W. R. Rees, *Biochem. J.,* **94,** 18 P (1965).

[56] P. N. Viswanathan, and P. S. Krishnan, *Indian J. Biochem.,* **2,** 69 (1965).

molecules *de novo* (see also p. 100), the implication is that amylose is formed first and then may be branched to amylopectin, and that this happens in the stroma outside the starch granule. There is some biochemical evidence to support this contention (see p. 72).[57] After injection of ^{14}C-labeled sugars into wheat plants an investigation of the endosperm starch showed that the radioactivity went first into amylose, which then lost much of its radioactivity to amylopectin, especially in the beginning stages of development. Once the starch granule had crystallized out there was no turnover, so that the conversion of amylose to amylopectin took place before the deposition. These results are in agreement with apposition by means of coacervate droplets in which the reactions, leading to starch formation, take place. As a result one expects amylose and amylopectin to be intimately mixed together and to show a regular distribution throughout the starch granule. (Evidence for such a distribution is discussed on p. 85.) In addition wheat starch was found to contain about 6 percent of a polymer with a degree of branching intermediate between amylose and amylopectin. The specific activity of this fraction was similar to that of the amylopectin and it was therefore either an incomplete or a degraded amylopectin. Some evidence is available that would favor the first possibility (p. 69).

The postulated interaction with the glucosyl transferase in preventing amylose from becoming branched, would also take place in the stroma. If most of the action occurs in the stroma then the amount of protein found inside the starch granules should bear no relationship to either amylose content or ADPG-glucosyl transferase activity, and this is indeed the case. Such relationships might well exist in the coacervate droplets.

It is significant that the same arguments, discussed above, have been used as supporting evidence for a mechanism of starch formation in which it is proposed that glycogen should be the precursor.[58] There seem to be more speculations than data in this field, and all one can do is to judge which theory is best supported by experimental evidence, and hope for more of the latter.

Various authors have reported different amounts of protein in

[57] W. B. McConnell, A. K. Mitra, and A. S. Perlin, *Canad. J. Biochem. Physiol.*, **36**, 985 (1958); and R. L. Whistler and J. R. Young, *Cereal Chem.*, **37**, 204 (1960).
[58] S. R. Erlander and H. L. Griffin, *Stärke*, **19**, 34 (1967).

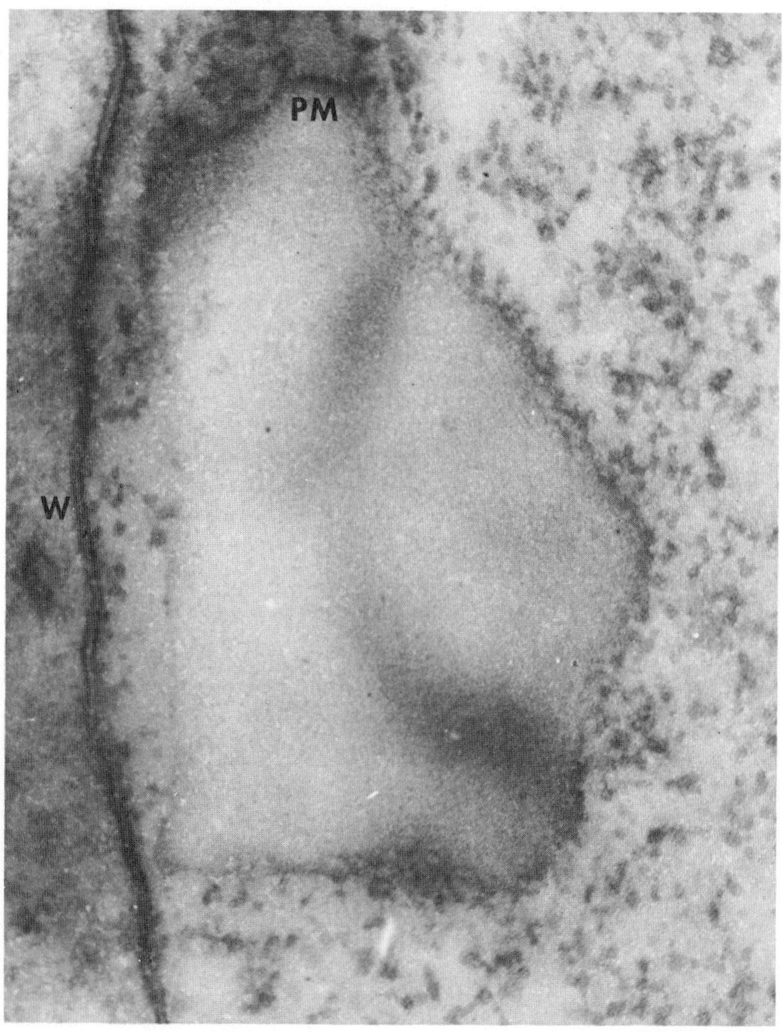

FIG. 2-1. Ultrathin section through a starch granule in a plastid from the endosperm of sweet corn. The part adjacent to the plastidal wall (W) shows no growth, but particles from the stroma are incorporated into the opposite part, which is growing by apposition. A pseudo-membrane (PM) is visible in the top part. $KMnO_4$ fix. Prim. magnif. 80,000 ×.

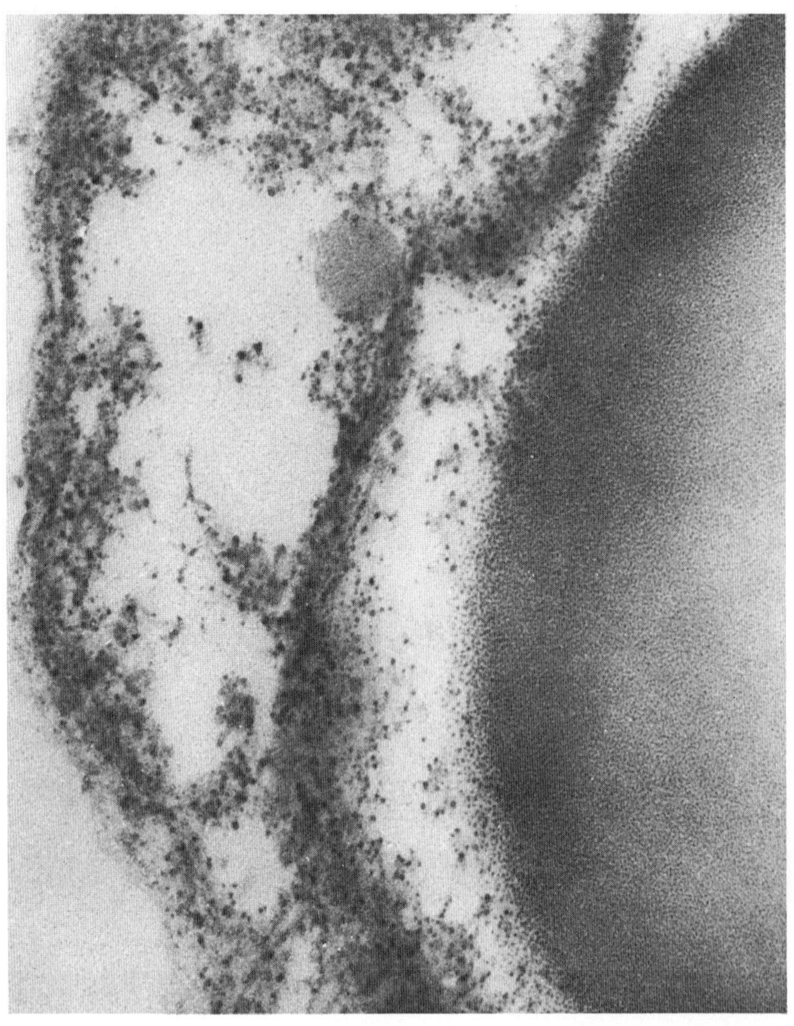

FIG. 2-2. Ultrathin section through part of a chloroamyloplast from a leaf of *Pellionia*. The periphery of the growing starch granule consists of small particles which are becoming incorporated. Larger particles in the stroma are ribosomes. Ryter-Kellenberger fix. Prim. magnif. 9200 ×. Photo: R. SALEMA.

the same starches.[59] Waxy corn contains protein, but no ADPG-glucosyl transferase. These observations provide additional reasons why there is no correlation between protein content and enzyme activity in starch. In addition proteins can be adsorbed and residues of the plastid may stick to the surface of the granule.[60]

The glucosyl transferase is so strongly adsorbed to the starch molecules in the granule, that it can not be washed out from the native starch granules. Even when the paracrystalline structure of the granule was opened by grinding in a buffer with pH 8.4, swelling in urea, or corroding with α-amylase—methods which increased the measured activity of glucosyl transferase (p. 30)—the enzyme remained bound to the undissolved part of the granules.[61] Glucosyl transferase was not released during the amylolytic degradation of assimilatory starch of green leaves in the dark or of the reserve starch in germinating seeds. The starch residues from germinating seeds lost their enzyme activity rapidly, probably because of the generally prevailing hydrolytic conditions in such organs,[62] more especially proteolytic action.

In conclusion, glucosyl transferase, and possibly other proteins, form an integral part of starch granule structure (pp. 70, 101). In this form its conformation is probably different from that of the enzyme in solution.[63]

59 R. B. Frydman, *Arch. Biochem. Biophys.*, **102**, 242 (1963); and C. T. Greenwood and J. Thomson, *J. Chem. Soc.*, 222 (1962).
60 A. T. Czaja, *Proplasma*, **46**, 143 (1956).
61 Frydman and Cardini, *op. cit.*
62 Chandorkar and Badenhuizen, *Cereal Chem.*, *op. cit.*
63 Frydman and Cardini, *op. cit.*

CHAPTER THREE

ORIGIN, MULTIPLICATION, AND GENETICS OF AMYLOPLASTS

ALTHOUGH SCHIMPER'S THEORY ABOUT THE CONTINUITY OF PLASTIDS BY means of division has been generally accepted, the possibility that plastids can also originate *de novo* is not excluded. So far the electron microscope has not been able to provide us with conclusive evidence for or against an origin *de novo,* so the question whether such an origin exists has to remain unanswered for the time being.[1]

An origin *de novo* is not necessarily in conflict with the genetic evidence for the autonomy of the plastid, which has been mainly derived from the study of chloroplasts. However, one may be justified in asking whether chloroplasts, with their highly specialized photosynthetic apparatus, are representative of the plastids in general. What is the function of the DNA in chloroplasts and their younger stages, the proplastids? What are the roles of the nuclear genes and the environment on chloroplast structure? And finally, do these factors have a bearing on the production of starch in general, and of reserve starch granules with recognizable shape in particular?

Gibor and Granick attempted to give answers to some of these questions, and concluded that an origin *de novo* disagrees with the bulk of available evidence.[2] Since much of this evidence had been derived from the study of *Euglena,* a unicellular alga which can lose its capability to develop chloroplasts from proplastids, and therefore,

[1] N. P. Badenhuizen, *Canad. J. Bot.,* **40,** 861 (1962); and M. Vesk, F. V. Mercer, and J. V. Possingham, *Austral. J. Bot.,* **13,** 161 (1965).

[2] A. Gibor and S. Granick, *Science,* **145,** 890 (1964).

is highly specialized, generalizations remain questionable. For that reason, and in order to stress the necessity for a continuing discussion on the subject, a few remarks about plastid origin *de novo* are made.

If an origin *de novo* exists, it may have different pathways. Some pictures seem to indicate that plastids could develop from small conglomerations of macromolecules[3] or from vesicles in the cytoplasm.[4] The existence of self-reproducing units in the cytoplasm, consisting of nucleic acids, has been postulated.[5] Such units could perhaps induce the formation of "initials," the smallest recognizable particles from which proplastids are derived,[6] and in this way genetic continuity would be maintained. Such a mechanism presupposes the occurrence of DNA in the cytoplasm, for which there is some evidence.[7] However, after labeling with ^{3}H-thymidine, much of the radioactivity may go into macromolecules other than DNA[8] and more experimentation is necessary.

Another mechanism has been suggested for the origin of plastids in the maturing egg cell of the bracken fern [*Pteridium aquilinum* (L.) Kuhn].[9] The old plastids were seen to degenerate and new ones were formed from evaginations of the nuclear membrane. In this case some autonomy could be brought about by a genetically controlled membrane composition (p. 42).

Although this replacement of old plastids by new ones was expected to be a general feature, no such phenomena could be detected in the comparable egg cells of the liverwort *Sphaerocarpus donnellii* Aust. or the fern *Dryopteris*[10] and the matter remains controversial.

3 Badenhuizen, *op. cit.*

4 H. Camefort in *Electron Microscopy*, S. S. Breese, ed., Vol. 2, NN7 (New York, Academic Press, 1962).

5 G. Brawerman and E. Chargaff, *Biochem. Biophys. Acta*, **37**, 221 (1960).

6 A. Frey-Wyssling and K. Mühlethaler, *Ultrastructural Plant Cytology* (Amsterdam, Elsevier, 1965).

7 P. R. Bell and K. Mühlethaler, *J. Mol. Biol.*, **8**, 853 (1964); J. Brachet, *Nature*, **213**, 650 (1967); A. M. de Recondo, C. Frayssinet, and J. J. de Recondo, *C. R. Acad. Sci. (Paris)*, **255**, 3471 (1962); and E. B. Mourad, *J. Cell Biol.*, **24**, 267 (1965).

8 A. Lima-de-Faria, *Hereditas*, **53**, 1 (1965); and M. Wand, E. Zeuthen, and E. A. Evans, *Science*, **157**, 436 (1967).

9 P. R. Bell, A. Frey-Wyssling, and K. Mühlethaler, *J. Ultrastruct. Res.*, **15**, 108 (1966); and K. Mühlethaler and P. R. Bell, *Naturwiss.*, **49**, 63 (1962).

10 L. Diers in *Probleme der biologischen Reduplikation*, P. Sitte, ed., 227 (Berlin, Springer, 1966); and W. Menke, *Z. Naturforsch.*, **19** b, 520 (1964).

The development of the chloroplast takes place in steps which are dependent on the presence of nuclear genes.[11] In addition chloroplasts, and related plastids, such as the virescent amyloplasts of potato, the chloroamyloplasts of *Pellionia* and other plants, chloroplasts degenerated to chromoplasts[12] and mutated chloroplasts,[13] all contain DNA, and form a family of plastids with specific properties. Light induces the production of nucleic acids independently of chlorophyll synthesis or photosynthesis.[14] The nucleic acids provide the chloroplast with its own system of protein production.[15] Among these proteins are the enzymes involved in starch synthesis. They disappear during a period of darkness (p. 100) and now the type of starch such starved chloroplasts will produce depends on the external conditions. In the light starch with about 20 percent amylose is formed, but when at the same time glucose is given, the starch produced consists mainly of amylopectin.[16] It is therefore possible to influence the reconstitution of the enzymes.

Leucoamyloplasts also contain DNA.[17] Whether green or colorless, amyloplasts always contain starch-synthesizing enzymes; the enzymes operate in the dark and are dependent upon an external carbohydrate supply for starch formation. In corn many genotypes are found that influence the composition and quantity of the starch formed in the endosperm.

We are inclined to conclude that the DNA in plastids has a subordinate role in providing for the maintenance of the stroma composition by making some of its specific enzymes, such as phosphorylase.[18] What, then, could be the mechanism that gives the stroma its specificity, independently of the complications found in chloroplasts?

That plastids divide is beyond doubt (see Figs. 1-6 and 5-3)

[11] D. von Wettstein and G. Eriksson, *Proc. 11th Internat. Congress of Genetics, the Hague, 1963,* 591 (1964).

[12] R. Salema and N. P. Badenhuizen, unpublished.

[13] H. Ris, *Fifth Internat. Congress of Electron Microscopy,* Vol. 2, XX-I (1962).

[14] H. Senger and N. I. Bishop, *Plant & Cell Physiol.* (Tokyo), **7,** 441 (1966).

[15] Brachet, *op. cit.;* and J. W. Davies and E. C. Cocking, *Biochem. J.,* **101,** 28 P (1966).

[16] K. Doi, A. Doi, and Z. Nikuni, *Stärke,* **18,** 281 (1966).

[17] Salema and Badenhuizen, unpublished.

[18] See also B. G. T. Pogo and A. O. Pogo, *J. Cell Biol.,* **22,** 296 (1964).

(p.61).[19] They also may produce buds[20] which can be pinched off and assume independence; however, since such buds show signs of degeneration, it is doubtful whether they would develop into mature plastids.[21] Sometimes it looks as if a division had started, but the process was halted, so that the constriction remained. If this process were repeated several times, bead-like plastids of the type shown in Figure 1-13 would be formed. Such plastids have also been found in *Isoetes*[22] and the nucellus in cotton.[23] In *Selaginella* the daughter plastids remain connected in chains, and are linked together by threads,[24] representing one further step to complete division. Similar chains can be produced artificially under the influence of rubidium chloride.[25]

The genetics of chloroplasts with their complex ultrastructure has been adequately covered in recent reviews in which the authors conclude that the chloroplast is very much dependent upon its cytoplasmic environment, which either maintains or affects the lamellar structure.[26] We know that light, temperature, and deficiencies influence chloroplast structure, and within certain limits these changes are reversible. If the cytoplasmic environment is changed as a consequence of nuclear gene mutation, the plastid structures are irreversibly affected. Similar ideas have been expressed by Bell *et al.*[27]

It is possible that the regulating mechanism which maintains a particular stroma composition is to be found in the membranes surrounding the plastid. These membranes contain specific proteins linked to specific lipids or mixtures of lipids in definite proportions, and it has been suggested that the composition of the membranes is genetically controlled.[28]

The concept of a static unit membrane as a bimolecular leaflet

19 Badenhuizen, *Canad. J. Bot., op. cit.;* and Diers, *op. cit.*

20 Badenhuizen, *ibid.;* and B. Sprey and H. Weinert, *Z. Naturforsch.,* **21** b, 72 (1966).

21 F. Schötz and L. Diers, *Planta,* **66**, 269 (1965).

22 D. J. Paolillo, *Amer. J. Bot.,* **49**, 590 (1962).

23 W. A. Jensen, *J. Ultrastruct. Res.,* **13**, 112 (1965).

24 H. Reinhard, *Protoplasma,* **19**, 541 (1933).

25 H. Lärz, *Flora,* **135**, 319 (1942).

26 Wettstein and Eriksson, *op. cit.;* D. Wilkie, *The Cytoplasm in Heredity* (London, Methuen, 1964); and J. T. O. Kirk and R. A. E. Tilney-Bassett, *The Plastids* (London, San Francisco: Freeman and Co., 1967).

27 Bell, Frey-Wyssling, and Mühlethaler, *op. cit.*

28 A. L. Lehninger, *Naturwiss.,* **53**, 57 (1966).

of lipids, coated by proteins, has been widely accepted, but was recently criticized. Korn[29] and other investigators[30] point to the many different functions of biological membranes. Such diversity could be understood better if the proteins are considered to be the functional units, rather than a rigid arrangement of lipid molecules. The biogenetic sequence could be the genetically controlled production of specific proteins, their combination with lipids as directed by amino acid sequence, followed by aggregation of the lipo-proteins so formed into lamellar structures with globular subunits. In living cells a certain mobility of the constituting molecules will add to the flexibility of the membrane structure, which is to be considered dynamic rather than static. The two membranes surrounding the plastid differ in function and therefore, most likely, also in structure.

Nuclear control of membrane composition would account for selective admission of raw material stroma for formation, including the synthesis of a number of proteins by plastidal DNA. As a consequence, gene mutations could affect quantity and conformation of these proteins.

Such a mechanism would allow amyloplasts in different plant species to build up their own stroma under the direct influence of the nucleus as modified by cell differentiation, with the starch granule as the final reflection of processes started in nuclear genes.

29 E. D. Korn, *Science,* **153,** 1491 (1966).
30 D. F. H. Wallach and P. H. Zahler, *Proc. Nat. Acad. U. S.,* **56,** 1552 (1966).

Part TWO

THE BIOGENESIS OF SPECIAL STARCHES

CHAPTER FOUR

STARCH GRANULES FROM VARIOUS SOURCES

ONLY A DOZEN OF THE MANY TYPES OF STARCH GRANULES DESCRIBED IN two extensive works[1] are considered in the following pages. A modest beginning therefore, but nevertheless the results obtained with these few starches constitute all of our present knowledge of starch formation.

The differences in fine structure of the starch granules from different plants, resulting from the condition of their biogenesis, are still far from being understood. The answer to this problem will probably be found in the molecular biology of starch formation, the relation between nucleic acids and certain proteins, and the complexes formed between these proteins and the polysaccharides.

4-1. THE DIFFERENCES BETWEEN SO-CALLED TUBER AND CEREAL STARCHES

The cereal starches are derived from the endosperm of grass seeds, irrespective of whether these grasses are cultivated or not. Understandably, starch from cereals such as corn, wheat, rye, barley, and rice, which are among our main food plants, has been studied most extensively. In contrast, the tuber starches comprise those of

[1] E. T. Reichert, *Carnegie Inst. Publ.,* 173 (1913); and J. Seidemann, *Stärke-Atlas* (Berlin, Hamburg, Paul Parey, 1966).

tubers, bulbs and rhizomes. How valid is this distinction between tuber and cereal starches?

Superficially the difference can be found in the crystalline pattern, as reflected in the x-ray spectrum—the cereal starches showing an *A*-diagram, and the tuber starches a *B*-diagram. However, high amylose corn starch produces a *B*-diagram, and a tuber starch may have an *A*-spectrum, as in the case of *Colocasia*. A stem starch may have an *A*-spectrum (*Dieffenbachia*) or a *B*-spectrum (*Pellionia*).[2] If starch granules are stained with acridine orange and then viewed in ultraviolet light, some will emit a red, others a green fluorescence. The "red" and the "green" group correspond quite well with the *A* and the *B* group, the notable exception being potato starch with red fluorescence and a *B*-diagram.[3]

Potato tuber starch can be converted into a cereal-type by applying a heat-moisture treatment[4] or by heating with 69 percent diacetone alcohol.[5] During this process swelling power and solubility decrease, and the *B*-spectrum becomes an *A*-spectrum. The change is attributed to an increase in associative bonding between neighboring molecules.

Evidently a subdivision into tuber and cereal starch is an arbitrary one. The most obvious differences are in the crystalline pattern, and this is determined mainly by the conditions under which the starch granules are deposited and develop. It seems that a shortage of hydration water leads to closer association between the molecules, caused by an increased number of hydrogen bonds between OH-groups of adjacent molecules (p. 51). This creates the necessary conditions for adsorption of cationic basic dyes, presumably through negative charges. As soon as the starch granules swell, these properties are lost and the granules can now be stained with anionic acid stains.[6]

Other characteristics which are correlated with the two main types of x-ray diffraction pattern, and factors that influence their transformation, are discussed in the following.

Increased molecular association (or retrogradation) can be effected by heating starch granules in an excess of water just below the

[2] N. P. Badenhuizen, *Stärke*, **17**, 69 (1965).
[3] *Ibid.*
[4] L. Sair, *Cereal Chem.*, **44**, 8 (1967).
[5] H. W. Leach, L. D. McCowen, and J. Schoch, *Cereal Chem.*, **36**, 534 (1959).
[6] Badenhuizen, *op. cit.*

swelling temperature or with little water at higher temperatures. Increased association is also promoted by a certain optimal chain length. In addition fatty substances may be present, such as the phospholipids in wheat starch,[7] which also contribute to a decrease in swelling power.[8] The complex mixture in the stroma of the plastid not only determines the chemical composition of the starch granules it forms, but also the molecular association and the crystalline pattern. These properties can be further influenced by external conditions. When soybean seedlings were grown at various temperatures, their starch showed a shift from the *B*-diagram in the direction of the *A*-diagram over the intermediate *C*-spectrum as the temperature was increased from 10°C to 40°C.[9] No such shift was found for starch from potato tubers aseptically grown on stem pieces (p. 90); at all temperatures the x-ray spectrum was a typical *B*-diagram.[10]

High temperature may influence the size and the shape of the starch granule. Cobs of waxy corn were cut from the plant on the tenth day after pollination, when starch production is just beginning (p. 57). They were then placed in 4 percent sucrose solutions in incubators at various temperatures. At 10°C growth was inhibited and no progress in development was noticeable [Fig. 4-1(a)]. At 30°C the starch granules were retarded in growth and many had abnormal shapes [Fig. 4-1 (b) and (c)]. There was no change in the *A*-spectrum as temperatures increased, but the starch developed at 30°C had a higher birefringence end point than that grown at 24°C. Consequently, even in starches with an *A*-spectrum some additional retrogradation is possible. In nature an increase in retrogradation is observed during the development of the starch granules of wheat, corn, and other cereals (p. 71).

The conversion of *A*-starch into *B*-starch has not been realized in the intact granule. Disruption of associative bonding leads to swelling, which for the native starch granule is an irreversible process, limited only by the number of disruptions.[11] The expression "grown structure"[12] or "primary resistance"[13] has been used to in-

[7] J. Washüttl, J. Hölzl, and E. Bancher, *Z. Pflanzenphysiol.*, **55**, 20 (1966).
[8] N. P. Badenhuizen, *Bakers' Dig.*, **25**, 21 (1951).
[9] S. Hizukuri, M. Fujii, and Z. Nikuni, *Nature,* **192**, 239 (1961).
[10] F. H. Zobel, personal communication.
[11] K. Linsbauer, *Beih. Bot. Cbl.*, **53** A, 172 (1935).
[12] N. P. Badenhuizen, *Protoplasma;* **28**, 293 (1937).
[13] N. P. Badenhuizen, *Cereal Chem.*, **32**, 286 (1955).

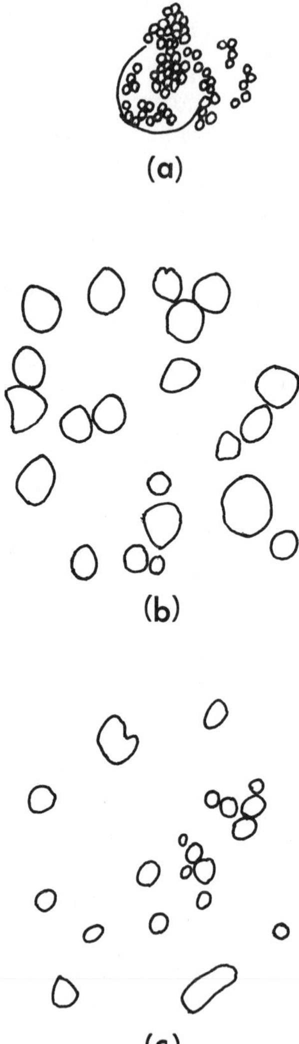

FIG. 4-1. Starch granules from the endosperm of waxy corn cobs grown on a 4% sucrose solution at different temperatures. (a) 10°C, (b) 24°C, (c) 30°C. The magnification of (a) is ⅔ that of (b) and (c).

dicate the associative forces between molecules in the native starch granule. Slight disruptions of these forces as an introduction to swelling in parts of the granule can be detected in starch granules that give red fluorescence in ultraviolet light after staining with acridine orange. In those parts the fluorescence color has shifted to green, although no changes can be detected in the granules when they are studied in ordinary light.[14]

Green fluorescence of acridine orange in ultraviolet light is caused by the undissociated molecule or by a low concentration of the chromogenic cation.[15] Since undissociated molecules of acridine orange exist only at pH 8.6 or higher, *B*-starches must be green-fluorescing because of low cation concentration or lack of negative charges. In potato starch with *B*-spectrum acridine orange cation accumulation is probably caused by the negatively charged esterified phosphate groups in the amylopectin fraction; one would expect dephosphorylated potato starch to have green fluorescence. That esterified phosphate is responsible for some of the unique features of potato starch, has been recognized for a long time and is supported by the fact that in acridine orange, red-fluorescing potato starch granules do not "fade" to green under the influence of the ultraviolet radiation, whereas all *A*-starches do change their color. Potato starch is therefore an exception, as in so many other respects. Attempts to revert green fluorescing starches to red were negative.

To answer the question why *B*-starches are not able to accumulate cations from basic dyes such as acridine orange, we recall the experiments of Hellman, Fairchild, and Senti.[16] Gels were made by heating wheat starch for thirty minutes at 95°C with various quantities of water, and were then allowed to age for eight days under conditions which prevented loss of water. The x-ray analysis gave the following results: gels with less than 29 percent water had an *A*-spectrum, those containing 32 to 39 percent water a *C*-spectrum, and at water contents of 43 percent and higher a *B*-spectrum appeared. With more than 56 percent water recrystallization was difficult.

The explanation has been as follows. When the number of water molecules is insufficient to compete for the free OH-groups of

[14] N. P. Badenhuizen, *Stärke,* **17,** 69 (1965).
[15] A. T. Czaja, *Stärke,* **13,** 357 (1961).
[16] N. N. Hellman, B. Fairchild, and F. R. Senti, *Cereal Chem.,* **31,** 495 (1954).

the starch molecules, an *A*-starch is produced. Beyond a certain percentage of water the OH-groups of one starch molecule are prevented from directly forming hydrogen bonds with the OH-groups of other molecules. The OH-groups now become masked by water molecules, which in turn, by forming hydrogen bonds among themselves, still may bring about sufficient adhesion between the starch molecules to keep them in an ordered pattern, and this gives an x-ray diffraction pattern of the *B*-type. Of course, other forces between molecules play a role as well,[17] but the hydrogen bonds are considered to be the most important for this discussion.

The swelling power of a starch is determined by such factors as complex formation with fatty substances, and the amount of amylose, irrespective of the x-ray diagram. A high amylose corn starch, for instance, has a *B*-spectrum, but very low swelling power. Therefore the best distinction between starches in general is provided by x-ray analysis, and, within certain limits, the ultraviolet fluorescence color after staining with acridine orange.

A-starches have less water sorption than *B*-starches.[18] Arranged in order of increased sorption, Kapp *et al.* gave the following list: wheat, tapioca, corn (20 percent amylose), rice, corn (5 percent amylose), retrograded corn starch, *Maranta* (arrowroot), corn (80 percent amylose), potato. The first five of these starches are of the *A*-type, the others are *B*-starches. This order does not apply to the rapidity of the swelling. Normal corn starch and waxy corn starch, for instance, have the same range of gelatinization temperatures, but the waxy variety swells more rapidly.[19] Linear expansion of vacuum-dry starch granules, measured in a water-saturated atmosphere, gave the following increases: normal corn, 9.1 percent; potato, 12.7 percent; tapioca, 28.4 percent; and waxy corn, 22.7 percent.[20] The initial rapid swelling of tapioca and waxy corn starch granules is evident; they must have a similar physical structure and the structural disposition of the water is probably alike in these two starches, although their chemistry differs. For that reason tapioca could be

[17] A. Frey-Wyssling and K. Mühlethaler, *Ultrastructural Plant Cytology* (Amsterdam, Elsevier, 1965).

[18] M. Kapp, C. Legrand, and O. Yovanovitch, *C. R. Acad. Sci.* (*Paris*), **255**, 2967 (1962); and Sair, *op. cit.*

[19] T. J. Schoch and E. C. Maywald, *Anal. Chem.*, **28**, 382 (1956).

[20] N. N. Hellman, T. F. Boesch, and E. H. Melvin, *J. Amer. Chem. Soc.*, **74**, 348 (1952).

replaced with waxy corn after World War II when the Indonesian source of tapioca dried up.

Processes similar to those found for the aging of starch gels under experimental conditions, must take place in the amyloplasts. Although the stroma has the properties of a liquid, its viscosity may be considerable. We would expect that the viscosity of the stroma of amyloplasts producing *A*-starch is higher than that of amyloplasts producing *B*-starch. The number of water molecules available for crystallization of starch will be determined by the amount of water bound to other molecules in the stroma. There will be less free water in "*A*-stroma" than in "*B*-stroma."

The combination of an amylose content not much exceeding 25 percent, a low percentage of proteins, fatty substances, and other minor constituents, should allow for a compact alignment of starch molecules accompanied by high swelling power in a *B*-starch. This was confirmed for potato starch by the work of Leach, McCowan, and Schoch,[21] who also demonstrated that corn starch swells much more freely after defatting. A series of starches can be drawn up showing increasing swelling power, culminating in the rapid swelling of potato starch, where it is enhanced by the presence of esterified phosphate groups.

In a potato starch granule with a very low protein and fat content, the molecular network is scarcely disturbed by these non-starch constituents. The result is an extremely regular swelling of all parts of the granule. The spaces between the starch molecules allow penetration of substances with a molecular weight smaller than 1000 after imbibition of the granules with water.[22] No doubt such pores will be narrower in the dry granule, and slightly swollen starch granules will admit larger molecules. Since protein molecules can not penetrate potato starch granules (p. 34), the action of amylases takes place on the outside of the potato starch granule, proceeding slowly, but equally, at all sides. Such exocorrosion is rare for reserve *B*-starches and only found in those with large, eccentric granules showing pronounced layering, such as potato, *Canna, Lilium candidum, Phajus,*[23] and *Pellionia* (Fig. 4-2).[24] Other starches with less swelling

21 Leach, *et al., op. cit.*
22 G. H. Lathe and C. R. J. Ruthven, *Biochem. J.*, **62**, 665 (1956).
23 G. Krabbe, *Jb. wiss. Bot.*, **21**, 250 (1890).
24 A. Binz, *Flora*, **76**, 34 (1892).

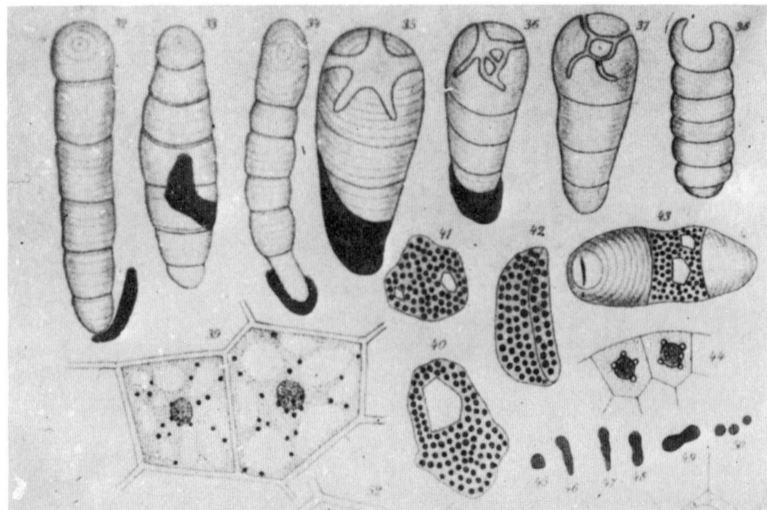

FIG. 4-2. Starch granules and plastids in the stem of *Pellionia*. Top row: the three granules to the left show exocorrosion, the others both endo- and exocorrosion. Black patches represent plastid residues. Grana are indicated by dots in four chloroamyloplasts, one of which is common to two starch granules. In a few cells the original arrangement of the proplastids around the nucleus (right) and their subsequent migration into the cytoplasm (left) has been drawn. After BINZ (1892).

power, including those from grass endosperms, cotyledons of *Leguminosae,* rhizome of *Iris* and bulbs of tulips, hyacinths, and daffodils, all show endocorrosion, the amylolytic enzymes penetrating into the interior of the granules. It is interesting to note that small potato starch granules, which have much less swelling power than the large ones, also are degraded by means of endocorrosion.[25]

It is likely that the type of corrosion is linked to the porosity that starch granules possess when they are imbibed with water. If, because of the presence of a certain amount of fatty substances or because of strong molecular association, the starch molecules are prevented from maintaining a coherent network during the imbibition with water, irregular swelling will take place with the result

[25] Krabbe, *op. cit.*

that faults are formed. Along those faults hydration of OH-groups will take place, making the starch molecules more available to amylolytic attack. Some of these faults may be wide enough to allow the action of amylases to proceed in a centripetal direction; they are then transformed into corrosion canals. Porosity of the tiny leaf starch granules which have a *B*-spectrum (p. 96)[26] must be negligible since they show exocorrosion.[27]

The x-ray spectra of starches bear no relation to the organs or tissues from which the starches were isolated, nor do they correspond to fixed patterns of swelling or amylolytic behavior. A division into tuber and cereal starches has little meaning, but a classification into *A*-, *B*- and *C*-starches is valuable, mainly because it is noncommittal. The composition of the amyloplast determines which type of starch granule will be produced, and will also influence its swelling and corrosion behavior.

We should bear in mind that the *C*-pattern represents a structure intermediate between the *A*- and *B*-spectra, or a mixture of them. Reports on x-ray spectra of some starches have been contradictory, and as a result tapioca has been moved from *C* to *A* and arrowroot from *C* to *B*.[28] As a type group *C*-starches are less reliable.

[26] F. H. Zobel, personal communication.
[27] N. P. Badenhuizen, *Protoplasma,* **62,** 306 (1966).
[28] C. Legrand and O. Yovanovitch, *C. R. Acad. Sci.* (*Paris*), **245,** 1553 (1957).

CHAPTER FIVE

A - STARCHES

5-1. CORN (*ZEA MAYS* L.)

THE CORN PLANT IS ESPECIALLY SUITED TO THE STUDY OF STARCH BIOgenesis because so much is known about its genetics. The occurrence of mutations influencing starch structure is a unique feature of *Zea*. A recent review of the influence of various genes and their combinations on starch production in corn has been given by Zuber.[1] Many genotypes are available for study and this circumstance should make the approach to enzymology and starch granule structure more exact and fruitful than for any other plant. Pictures of starch granules controlled by the genes *ae*, su_1 and su_2 or their combinations have been published by Sandstedt[2] and Badenhuizen.[3]

A detailed study of the development of corn endosperm showed that on the ninth to tenth day after pollination dramatic events take place.[4] The nucleus swells considerably, indicating increased metabolic activity, and the plastids move towards its periphery [see Fig. 4-1(a)]. At the same time the plastids form starch granules and often divide (Fig. 5-1, also Fig. 5-3). After some time they again become scattered in the cytoplasm (*cf.* p. 92). This process is first visible in the upper central part of the endosperm where cells mature earlier; gradually the zone of maturation descends.

[1] R. L. Whistler and E. F. Paschall, ed., *Starch: Chemistry and Technology*, vol. 1 (New York, Academic Press, 1965).

[2] R. M. Sandstedt, *Cereal Sci. Today*, **10**, 305 (1965).

[3] N. P. Badenhuizen, *Protoplasmalogia*, **2**. B. 2 b δ (1959); see also M. J. Wolf, H. L. Seckinger and R. J. Dimler, *Stärke* **16**, 375 (1964).

[4] L. Lampe, *Bot. Gaz.*, **91**, 337 (1931).

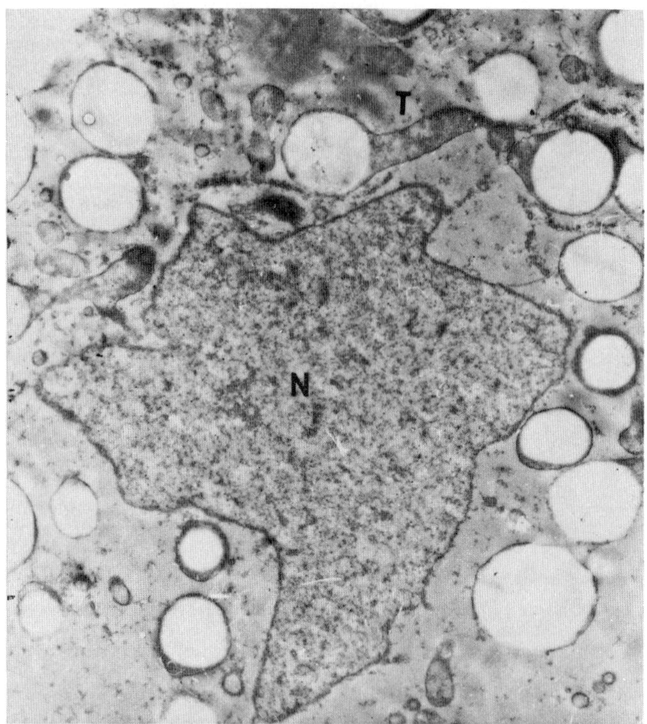

FIG. 5-1. Ultrathin section through a lobed nucleus (N), surrounded by amyloplasts, in an endosperm cell of corn, genotype sh_2su_2, 9 days after pollination. Most of the plastids are occupied by a simple starch granule, but in some the stroma is still visible. The shape of one amyloplast is filiform; it looks as if the starch granule it contains carries a tail (T). Glutaraldehyde and $KMnO_4$ fix. Prim. magnif. 2000 ×.

While the polysaccharides are deposited the water content of the fruit begins to decrease and may drop from 87 percent to 10 percent during maturation. The largest increase in starch granule size takes place during the first three weeks; at the same time their amylose content goes up to about 24 percent.[5]

In the fully mature starch, granules with a diameter of about

[5] M. J. Wolf, M. M. MacMasters, J. E. Hubbard, and C. E. Rist, *Cereal Chem.*, **25**, 312 (1948).

14μ take up the average weight; granules smaller than 8μ constitute 45 percent of the total number of granules, but they represent less than 8 percent of total weight.[6]

Since the receptivity of the silk for pollen, and later the loss of receptivity, proceeds from the base of the ear to the tip, the development of the kernels proceeds in the same direction. In other words, the younger kernels are situated nearer the tip of the ear; and starch development is in step with the stage of kernel development. It is not surprising that amylose content decreases in the endosperms from the base to the tip.[7]

The plastids show little or no structure (see Figs. 1-13 and 5-3), but vesicles and lamellar residues may be present to various extents. Sometimes these are arranged in circular fashion, making a complete or incomplete ring (Fig. 5-2, also Fig. 1-5). Starch granules originate

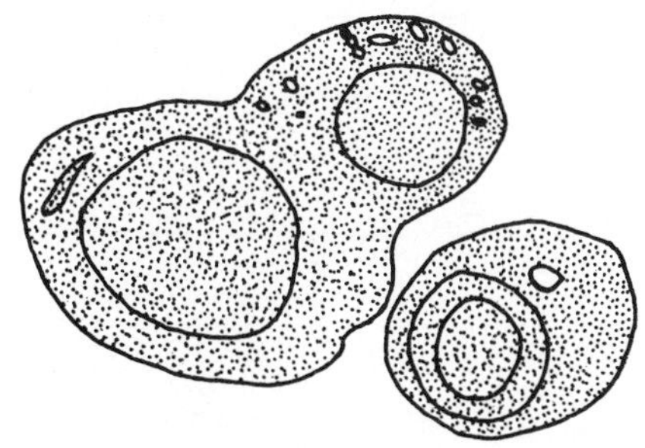

FIG. 5-2. Drawing from an ultrathin section through plastids in an endosperm cell of sweet corn. Ring-shaped lamellar structures will act as "pockets" for starch granule formation. Prim. magnif. 8000 ×.

by preference in the areas (pockets) provided by such structures, where enzymes and substrates appear to concentrate—presumably because diffusion is prevented. Eventually most of these structural features disappear.[8] The starch granule reproduced in Figure 2-1 demonstrates clearly that abundant growth is taking place away from, not near, the plastidal envelope. Little precursor material is

[6] T. J. Schoch and E. C. Maywald, *Anal. Chem.*, **28**, 382 (1956).
[7] V. L. Fergason, J. L. Helm, and M. S. Zuber, *Crop Sci.*, **6**, 273 (1966).
[8] N. P. Badenhuizen, *Proc. Kon. Nederl. Akad. Wetensch.*, **65** C, 123 (1962).

present between the double membrane and the granule, but there is an abundance of this material in the center of the stroma. Figure 6-8 shows that membranes are not involved in starch formation, but rather act as obstacles; the shape of assimilatory starch granules is determined by the space available.

Duvick described the presence of slender filaments among the plastids and concluded that plastids were derived from such filaments, which often showed swellings or knobs along their length.[9] No doubt Figures 1-13, 5-1, and 5-4 present pictures of such filaments. Although there are plastids with retarded division (see Fig. 1-13) the parts may eventually separate and attain independence.

Plastid division in young corn endosperm proceeds as follows.[10] First a constriction develops, as in Figures 1-6 and 5-3 and then the

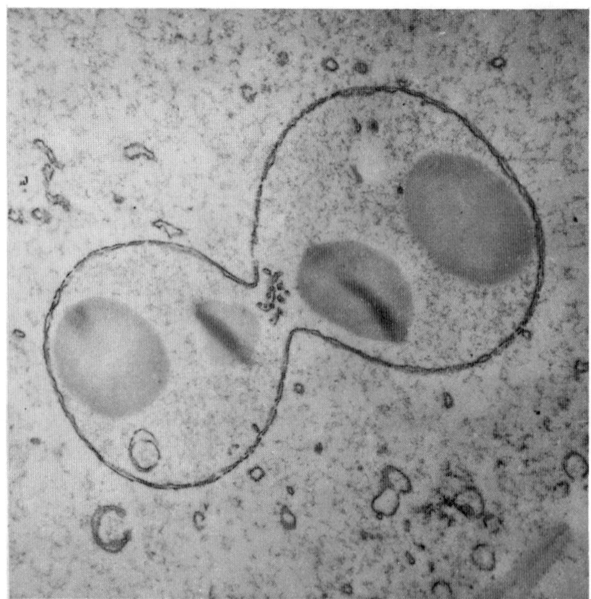

FIG. 5-3. Ultrathin section through a dividing amyloplast with starch granules in an endosperm cell of sweet corn. $KMnO_4$ treatment has caused breakages in the plastidal wall. Black patches in the granules are folds produced by the knife. Prim. magnif. 8000 ×.

[9] D. N. Duvick, *Bot. Gaz.*, **115**, 82 (1953).
[10] N. P. Badenhuizen, *Canad. J. Bot.*, **40**, 861 (1962).

two daughter plastids move in opposite directions, drawing out the constriction to a narrow canal, still limited by two unit membranes. Finally the connection snaps. The process of division does not seem to be hampered by the presence of starch granules in the plastids, and many divisions occur on the tenth day after pollination.

Not all plastids form starch at the same time. In the initial stages the amyloplasts closest to the nucleus may not have yet formed starch, while those somewhat farther away contain starch granules of various sizes. As the starch granules grow, ultrathin sections will show only one granule per plastid (see Fig. 5-1). but originally most plastids produce more than one granule (Fig. 5-3). The distribution of the granules during plastid divisions is such that eventually each daughter plastid receives only one granule. For that reason no compound starch granules are found in corn endosperm.

The average time of the first starch deposit is on the tenth day after pollination, but some plastids may start on the ninth day (see Fig. 5-1), while on the twelfth day many plastids may not yet have formed starch. The plastids in one cell are not synchronized in this respect. Detached cobs, grown on sucrose solution at 10°C, will remain at this stage with the amyloplasts clustered around the nucleus; whereas at room temperature they will develop normal starch granules [see Fig. 4-1(a), (b)]. The date of starch deposition is dependent on environmental factors and on the genotype.

The shape of the plastids is originally an elongated one, and many show multiple branching (Fig. 5-4). As starch granules grow in them, such plastids become shorter, the part containing the granule increasing in size. Sometimes this part may still be seen to carry a residue of the plastid as a little tail, as shown by one of the plastids in Figure 5-1.

The starch granules of waxy corn originate in the same way as those in normal corn starch. However, the first-formed deposits stain red with iodine, instead of blue; so they do not contain amylose but consist of amylopectin only.[11] Lampe was the first to observe a regional variety in the activity of waxy endosperms.[12] She found that in mature endosperms containing the recessive gene *wx* the starch granules in the central cap area stained red throughout with iodine

[11] Badenhuizen, *Protoplasmalogia, op. cit.;* and H. Fuwa, *Nature,* **176,** 159 (1957).

[12] Lampe, *op. cit.*

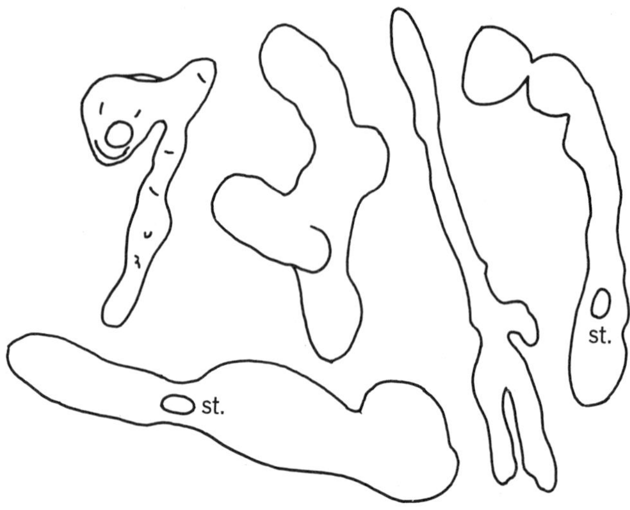

FIG. 5-4. Irregularly shaped plastids from young corn endosperm.

solution, but those farther away from this central region showed blue cores (shown in Figure 5-5 for waxy *Sorghum* starch where they are larger and more easily demonstrated than in waxy corn starch). These cores increased in size with distance; the small starch granules, produced at the base of the endosperm, and sometimes those beneath the aleuron layer, stained entirely blue. In other words, the amount of blue-staining material (presumably amylose) in the starch granules increased from the tip of the kernel towards the base.

This distribution does not coincide with the development of the starch granules in the endosperm. Except in one case, it was found that starch from the middle portion of the endosperm had the highest amylose percentage.[13] Since the amylose content is an indication of maturity, the starch granules situated in the middle part of the endosperm must be the oldest. It can not be maintained therefore that the "blue-staining" cores increase in size by intussusception as the waxy starch granule grows. The size of the core is

[13] Fergason *et al., op. cit.*

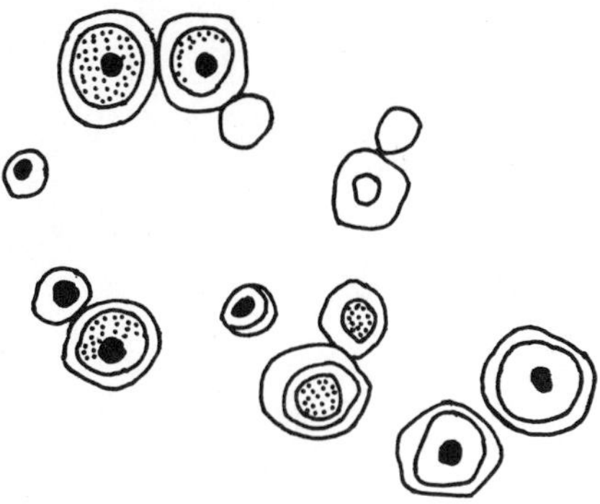

FIG. 5-5. Starch granules from waxy *Sorghum,* many showing a blue core after staining with iodine solution. 675 ×.

rather a consequence of cell differentiation, of biochemical differences between the cells in various parts of the endosperm. We could assume that the factors which protect amylose chains from becoming branched increase in quantity from cap to base, and it would be interesting to know whether there would be an increase in ADPG-glucosyl transferase in the same direction. We might also say that the influence of the *wx* gene becomes less in cells situated nearer the base of the endosperm, or at the end of the endosperm development.

It is easy to isolate the "blue cores" by lintnerization (treatment with 7.5 percent hydrochloric acid) of waxy starch, followed by staining with iodine and drying of the preparation.[14] Amylose-containing corn starch is little affected by lintnerization, in contrast to other starches it will stain blue with iodine even after prolonged treatment, and this property makes it possible to preserve the cores by the method mentioned, while the amylopectin is dissolved. Figure 5-6 shows cores isolated in this manner from waxy *Sorghum* starch. The variability in size is evident, and many cores are surrounded by a blue layer of less density. Whatever the process that deposits linear molecules in the center of the waxy starch granules, it seems to decrease gradually in intensity, after which it stops completely. It does not follow that nonwaxy starch granules, too, would contain less amylose at the periphery than in the center.

[14] N. P. Badenhuizen, *Cereal Chem.,* **32,** 286 (1955).

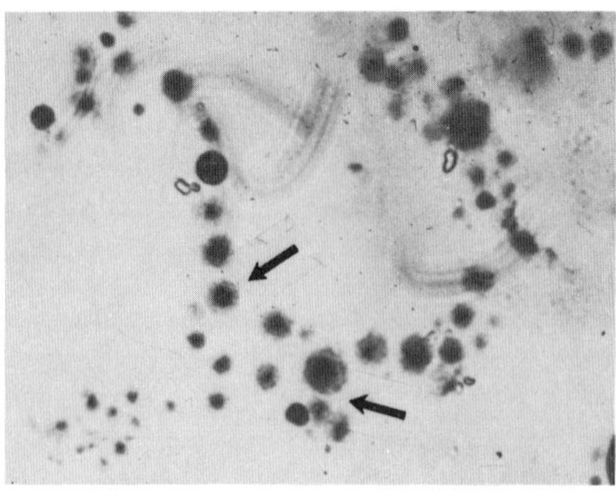

FIG. 5-6. "Blue-staining" cores isolated from waxy *Sorghum* starch. They vary in size and are often surrounded by less dense material (arrows).

When the first waxy starch granules are deposited on the tenth day after pollination, the pericarp of the corn fruit already contains starch, but the latter consists of normal "blue-staining" granules. At this moment starch granules appear in the pericarp cells which stain red with iodine, so these cells now contain a mixture of red- and blue-staining granules.[15] Such "mixed" cells are generally taken as proof that a plastid mutation has occurred, but in this case it is more likely that a change in cell metabolism, induced in the pericarp by the endosperm, has occurred and that the change is phenotypic. That neighboring cells of different genotype can have an influence on plastid structure was demonstrated by Abel.[16] Another example of phenotypic differences between plastids was recently found in *Nitella*.[17] The chloroplasts appear in rows which are derived by division from one plastid, and therefore any genotypic change in a plastid would affect a whole row. Some chloroplasts were unable to fix carbon dioxide but their distribution was at random, indicating that they only differed phenotypically from the majority of plastids; such chloroplasts also lacked the starch-synthesizing mechanism.

[15] Badenhuizen, *Protoplasmalogia, op. cit.*
[16] B. Abel, *Z. Bot.*, **50**, 60 (1962).
[17] A. Gibor, *Science*, **155**, 327 (1967).

Lintnerization produces pronounced layering in waxy corn starch granules, but much less so in the normal ones. In principle all reserve starches can be shown to be built up of shells, except when their structure is highly irregular, as is the case in some high-amylose corn starches (p. 102).[18]

A final amylose content of 24 percent is reached in corn starch during the first three weeks after pollination,[19] but the gelatinization temperatures continue to rise during further maturation, indicating an increased molecular association.[20] Loss of water is responsible for these physical changes, which, according to Schoch and Maywald, apply to small and large corn starch granules alike, so that both show the same gelatinization range. The result is a starch with decreased swelling power and sorption, which will show corrosion canals upon attack by amylases. Artificially one can demonstrate this by boiling corn starch in a solution of 2 ml sulfuric acid in 300 ml methanol. If a drop of the suspension is put on a slide and concentrated sulfuric acid is allowed to diffuse under the coverslip, the starch granules will show typical corrosion canals before they disintegrate.[21]

Electron micrographs of growing starch granules in glycogen maize (var. Golden Bantam) seem to indicate that apposition takes place through the incorporation of particles formed in the stroma (see Fig. 2-1).[22] These particles may be coacervate droplets, in which starch molecules or their precursors grow and accumulate. If they are the sites of starch formation then we may assume that the same fundamental process will take place in all the coacervate droplets in the stroma (p. 36). The way in which the molecules or their folds (p. 95) become oriented in a radial direction is at present unknown.

The subsequent increase in amylose content in the developing corn starch granule still can not be explained. Some investigators reason that, since the granule grows by apposition, each subsequent layer should contain more amylose, so that the periphery of the mature granule is richer in amylose than the center. In contrast, others contend that the periphery is richer in amylopectin; their opinion is

[18] Badenhuizen, *Cereal Chem., op. cit.;* and M. S. Buttrose, *Stärke,* **15,** 85 (1963).

[19] Wolf *et al., op. cit.*

[20] Schoch and Maywald, *op. cit.*

[21] N. P. Badenhuizen, *Recu. Trav. Bot. Néerl.,* **35,** 559 (1938).

[22] Badenhuizen, *Proc. Kon. Nederl. Akad. Wetensch., op. cit.*

based on the observation that the wall of the swollen starch granule mainly consists of amylopectin (p. 66).

Neither opinion need be true, nor does either necessarily explain the swelling phenomena observed in starch granules under the microscope. A consequence of the radial arrangement of the starch molecules is that swelling occurs in a tangential direction[23]—this explains all the events that take place during swelling. Since swelling is a physical process, no insight can be gained about the chemical composition of the various parts of a starch granule, nor can conclusions be drawn about the distribution of amylose in the granule. The swelling stages are the same for normal corn starch with 24 percent amylose as for waxy corn starch without amylose; they can be summarized as follows.

Water is taken up initially by the starch substance throughout the granule, and it is in this condition of imbibition that starch granules are found in plant cells. (For the formation of slight tangential dislocations at this stage, see p. 88 .) Upon further swelling the peripheral layers show a greater expansion than the central ones, since a given layer contains more molecules than the layer it surrounds. Because two layers are attached to each other the inner layer will be stretched to some extent; this effect will be more pronounced the more centrally a layer is situated. Therefore, mechanical damage is added to normal swelling in central layers and disruption of the molecular network will be greatest around the hilum of the granule as swelling proceeds. We can demonstrate this by adding congo red to the suspension—staining will start in the center of the granule.

Often wedge-shaped cracks are formed by this process (Fig. 5-7). At the same time a cavity develops and molecules, mainly amylose, from the disrupted inner layers diffuse into it. During the later stages of swelling the cavity is enlarged and the wall around it becomes composed mainly of the entangled amylopectin molecules, derived from all layers of the original starch granule. The final product is a thin-walled bladder.

These phenomena are physical changes brought about by the swelling mechanism; they bear no relation to the original distribution of amylose and amylopectin. The description applies to all starches with radial molecular arrangement, but variations arise ac-

[23] Badenhuizen, *Recu. Trav. Bot. Néerl., op. cit.;* and A. Meyer, *Untersuchungen über die Stärkekörner* (Jena, Fischer, 1895).

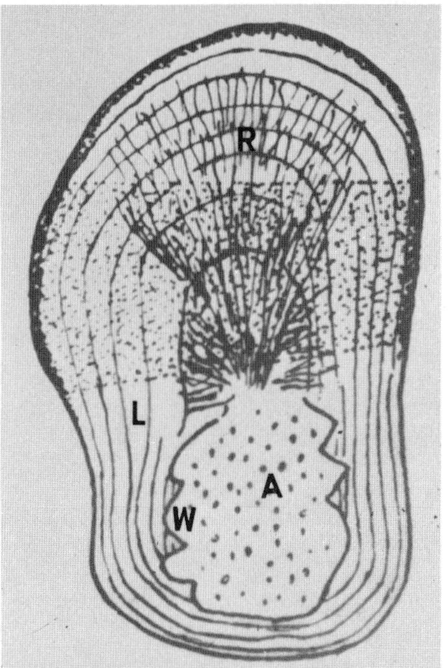

FIG. 5-7. Partially gelatinized potato starch granule. The distal part shows radial cracks (R). The proximal part (near the original hilum) is swollen. The layers (L) fuse together to form a wall of increasing amylopectin content around a cavity into which amylose (A) diffuses. The inside of the wall has wedge-shaped cracks (W).

cording to the particular shape of a granule, its swelling power, and the method of swelling. A corn starch granule may develop radial fissures, which, upon elongation, cut off segments; the layer fragments in these segments undergo tangential swelling, transforming the segments into globular pieces each of which initially may show a polarization cross. The starch granule has at this stage the appearance of a compound granule, but this is an artifact (Fig. 5-8).

Microscopic observations of the swelling of starch granules show all layers to be structurally equal. These observations, however, do not show whether the layers are chemically homogeneous (as many thought before 1940) or composed of an intimate mixture of amylose and amylopectin (as has since been found to be the case). Is it possible that the increase in the percentage of linear component could take place throughout the granule during its development?

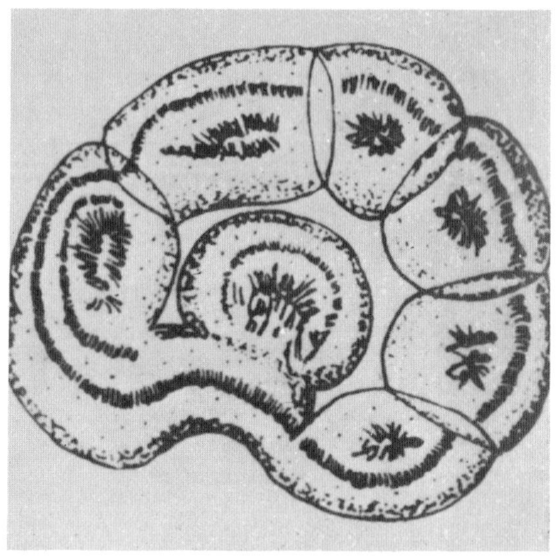

FIG. 5-8. Abnormal swelling of a corn starch granule, giving it the appearance of a compound granule.

Starch granules isolated from normal corn contain the enzyme ADPG-starch glucosyl transferase,[24] but the activity is lost during germination.[25] For dent corn we found in our laboratory an overall increase in ADPG-glucosyl transferase activity during the development of the starch in the endosperm. Since the enzyme is probably built in during the growth of the starch granule (p. 35) it would be available for the lengthening of some of the starch molecules by adding a glucose unit to the available nonreducing ends, resulting in an increase in the amount of apparent linear component by in-

[24] O. E. Nelson and H. W. Rines, *Biochem. Biophys. Res. Commun.*, 9, 297 (1962).

[25] K. R. Chandorkar and N. P. Badenhuizen, *Cereal Chem.*, 44, 27 (1967).

tussusception. For potato starch (p. 84) and pea starch (p. 105) it was found that the amylose molecules become longer and somewhat branched during the growth of the starch granules. This provides a strong argument for endogenous activity of enzymes like ADPG-glucosyl transferase and even some P- and Q-enzyme. Endogenous activity has been demonstrated for tapioca starch[26] and enzyme activity would continue while the starch granule grows by apposition. One might expect that intussusception would take place mainly in the more accessible amorphous layers. The process would stop when all free endgroups have become occupied and the available space has been filled. As a result all layers could well reach the same final amylose content (see also p. 103).

Waxy corn starch does not contain ADPG-glucosyl transferase.[27] Some investigators did not find much difference in protein content between waxy and normal corn starch (0.66 percent and 0.56 percent respectively),[28] but others found a large difference (0.10 percent and 0.83 percent).[29] We cannot, therefore, attach much value to the total protein content of starch in relation to enzyme activity (p. 37). It is interesting to note that the ratio between the P- and Q- enzymes is the same for both waxy and nonwaxy corn,[30] so that this ratio, by itself, can not furnish an explanation for the difference in chemical composition between the two starch types.

With the proteolytic enzyme pronase, derived from *Streptomyces griseus,* the particle weight of amylopectin from dent corn starch could be decreased considerably. This indicates that the amylopectin is complexed with proteins.[31] In addition seven percent of an intermediate type of amylopectin was found that did not form aggregates with proteins and which could be an interconversion product between amylose and amylopectin (p. 36). Since enzymes or proteins are supposed to have greater affinity for short than for long branches, the intermediate amylopectin should have longer free branches than the final amylopectin, suggesting that amylopectin

26 P. N. Viswanathan and P. S. Krishnan, *Indian J. Biochem.,* **2,** 16 (1965).

27 Nelson and Rines, *op. cit.;* and O. E. Nelson and C. Y. Tsai, *Science,* **145,** 1194 (1964).

28 Nelson and Rines, *ibid.*

29 C. T. Greenwood and J. Thomson, *J. Chem. Soc.,* 222 (1962).

30 H. Fuwa, *Arch. Biochem. Biophys.,* **70,** 157 (1957).

31 S. R. Erlander, J. P. McGuire and R. J. Dimler, *Cereal Chem,* **42,** 175 (1965).

is formed by increased branching of the intermediate fraction. At the same time this work[32] provides additional evidence for the existence of a protein network inside the starch granule (p. 37).

Some corn varieties, like *shrunken-2*[33] or *brittle-1* or *-2*[34] produce little starch in the endosperm, but contain considerable amounts of sucrose. It was recently found that these endosperms contain some UDPG-pyrophosphorylase, but no ADPG-pyrophosphorylase.[35] These enzymes produce UDPG, or ADPG, from G—1—P and UTP, or ATP. As a result of the deficiency, some UDPG will be formed, but no ADPG, and this has been related to the paucity of starch production. The greater efficiency of the ADPG-system, as compared to the UDPG-system, for the incorporation of glucose into starch molecules has been reported more than once for various starches.[36] Glucose can also be transferred to starch from sucrose in the presence of sucrose synthetase.[37] Unfortunately, all these experiments are based on the incorporation of glucose into existing starch molecules, and do not allow conclusions about the production of these starch molecules *ab initio*.

Several other genes suppress starch formation in corn and promote an increase in sugars; for instance the gene *ae*, and even more its combination with *wx*.[38] Various genotypes show significant differences in the distribution of carbohydrates. It is not known as yet what proteins or enzymes are affected by those genes, or how they influence starch synthesis.

Regardless of the type of starch that is present in the endosperm of the corn seed, the pericarp starch has always an *A*-type x-ray spectrum, although it may change to a *C*-type during maturation.[39] It has further been found that the glucosyl-transferase enzyme properties in the gametophytic tissues differ somewhat from those in the sporophytic tissues.[40] For an explanation of the difference in origin of both tissues, see Zuber.[41]

32 Erlander *et al., ibid.*
33 J. R. Laughnan, *Genetics,* **38,** 485 (1953).
34 J. W. Cameron and H. J. Teas, *Amer. J. Bot.,* **41,** 50 (1954).
35 C. Y. Tsai and O. E. Nelson, *Science,* **151,** 341 (1966).
36 R. B. Frydman, *Arch. Biochem. Biophys.,* **102,**, 242 (1963).
37 T. Akazawa, T. Minamikawa, and T. Murata, *Plant Physiol.,* **39,** 371 (1964).
38 R. G. Creech, *Genetics,* **52,** 1175 (1965).
39 F. H. Zobel, personal communication.
40 T. Akatsuka and A. E. Nelson, *J. Biol. Chem.,* **241,** 2280 (1966).
41 Whistler and Paschall, *op. cit.*

5-2. WHEAT (TRITICUM AESTIVUM L.)

The first starch granules deposited in the endosperm cells of wheat are often kidney-shaped; they later develop into large lenticular granules. About fourteen days after the first deposit new starch granules are formed in the same plastids, but these granules remain small. According to Buttrose the plastids produce evaginations resembling buds in which the small granules are found; eventually the buds are separated from the plastid by constriction.[42] Confirmation of such a separation could come only from serial sections, as has been done in the case of *Oenothera* plastids.[43] It is conceivable that the lack of development, or even the degeneration, displayed by such buds,[44] is a factor in determining the size of the starch granules.

During their development the large starch granules undergo a process of retrogradation which accompanies a simultaneous loss of water from the endosperm. The originally flexible and transparent structures now become rigid, show greater birefringence[45] and an increase in amylose content to 26 percent. The hilum is extended and eventually divides the granule into two cup-shaped parts which can easily be separated.[46]

In the native starch granule the layers are not distinct, but they can be made visible by treatment with diluted acid.[47] In 1926 van de Sande-Bakhuyzen found that starch granules had no layers if wheat plants were grown under constant environmental conditions.[48] His findings have recently been confirmed and extended by artificially inducing the formation of a few layers in the starch granule after subjecting it to two alternate applications of 24 hours darkness and 48 hours light. The number of layers formed corresponded to the dark–light periods; therefore the conclusion that the layering of

42 M. S. Buttrose, *Austral. J. Biol. Sci.,* **16,** 305 (1963).
43 F. Schötz and L. Diers, *Planta,* **66,** 269 (1965).
44 *Ibid.*
45 C. W. Bice, M. M. MacMasters, and G. E. Hilbert, *Cereal Chem.,* **22,** 463 (1945); and R. M. Sandstedt, *Cereal Chem.,* **23,** 337 (1946).
46 Badenhuizen, *Recu. Trav. Bot. Néerl., op. cit.*
47 Badenhuizen, *Cereal Chem., op. cit.*
48 H. L. van de Sande-Bakhuyzen, *Proc. Soc. Exper. Biol. Med.,* **23,** 302 (1926).

wheat starch granules is a direct consequence of the day–night alternations is justified.[49]

The homogeneous starch granules had the same amylose content as normal ones with layers. This constitutes further evidence for the essential similarity of the layers, each consisting of a densely crystalline and an amorphous part. It also supports the theory that starch formation takes place outside the granule in the stroma of the plastid (p. 36). If the molecules were lengthened in a continuous process at the periphery of the granule, they would extend from center to periphery. There is no evidence for the existence of such long molecules. On the contrary, the essentially similar composition of granules with and without layers shows that amylose and amylopectin molecules are no artifacts.

Phospholipids and amino acids have been found in wheat starch and were thought to be plastid residues.[50] The protein content averages 0.35 percent, but no studies on ADPG-glucosyl transferase or phosphorylase activity in wheat kernels have been published.

A waxy mutation, as found in corn, sorghum, rice, and barley, has not been discovered in wheat.

For experiments with wheat plants which indicate that the pathway to amylose is a more direct one than that to amylopectin, see p. 36.

5-3. BARLEY (HORDEUM VULGARE L.)

The development of large lenticular and small round starch granules in barley endosperm follows the same pattern as in wheat. The small granules are formed in buds which eventually may separate from the mother plastid.[51] The large starch granules are kidney-shaped and very transparent in the youngest stages. This shape may be determined by contact with lipid structures in the plastid, since the granules were found to have an indentation in the vicinity of such structures.[52] Lipid membranes may act as obstacles to the extension of the starch granule (p. 60).

49 M. S. Buttrose, *J. Cell Biol.*, **14**, 159 (1962).
50 J. Washüttl, J. Hölzl, and E. Bancher, *Z. Pflanzenphysiol.*, **55**, 20 (1966).
51 M. S. Buttrose, *J. Ultrastruct. Res.*, **4**, 231 (1960).
52 *Ibid.*

As in wheat, barley plants grown under constant environmental conditions form starch granules in the endosperm that lack layering, so that the latter is a consequence of day–night alternations.

May and Buttrose made a study of the development of the large starch granules in barley endosperm.[53] They found that the layers become more crowded towards the periphery, and they concluded that the peripheral layers differed in structure from the central ones because their swelling behavior was different. As discussed before (p. 66), conclusions about structure can not be drawn from observations on changes in starch granules produced during swelling.

During the first seven to eight weeks of development the amylose content of the large starch granules increases from 14 percent to 25 percent.[54] Environmental conditions and cultural practices did not have a great influence on final amylose percentage, which showed only minor variations. Some of the more marked differences in amylose content have been ascribed to differences between genotypes.[55] Recently a variety with starch of high amylose content (44 percent) was found.[56]

Starch granules of waxy barley endosperm contain centrally located material, which stains blue with an iodine solution, but whereas such blue-staining cores are always small in waxy varieties of corn and sorghum starch, the extent of these cores in waxy barley may vary.[57] If we assume that the cores are produced by a small inclusion of ADPG-glucosyl transferase (p. 63) the quantity of the enzyme in the cores may be too small for measurement by present methods. It is also possible that the activity disappears, since mature nonwaxy starch granules of barley and wheat show little or no ADPG-glucosyl transferase activity.[58] A study of the development of these starches in relation to changes in transferase activity would be useful.

Buttrose, studying lintnerized barley starch, concluded that the center of the starch granules was more resistant than the periphery and therefore should contain a higher amylose content.[59] However,

[53] L. H. May and M. S. Buttrose, *Austral. J. Biol. Sci.*, **12**, 146 (1959).
[54] G. Harris and I. C. MacWilliam, *Cereal Chem.*, **35**, 82 (1958).
[55] K. J. Goering, R. F. Eslick, and C. A. Ryan, *Cereal Chem.*, **34**, 437 (1957).
[56] N. R. Merritt, *J. Inst. Brew.*, **76**, 583 (1967).
[57] Badenhuizen, *Protoplasmalogia*, *op. cit.*
[58] Chandorkar and Badenhuizen, *op. cit.*
[59] Buttrose, *J. Cell Biol.*, *op. cit.*

even if all layers have the same composition, the greater swelling power of the separated peripheral layers would make them more accessible to the action of acid (p. 66).[60]

The influence of nuclear genes on the structural composition of plastids has been demonstrated clearly in barley. In a series of publications von Wettstein has shown that gene mutations have the effect of stopping the development of the chloroplast at various stages.[61] Such mutations have not only been found in Monocotyledons (to which group grasses, such as barley, belong) but also in Dicotyledons, for instance *Arabidopsis*[62] and tomato.[63] They cause deficiencies some of which could be overcome by the addition of certain amino acids. The blocks are evidently in the enzyme systems and proteins necessary for the formation and maintenance of the lamellar structures. Those enzymes and proteins in the stroma, which are involved in starch synthesis, can probably be affected similarly.

5-4. RICE (ORYZA SATIVA L.)

The starch granules in rice endosperm are compound. Many granules are produced in the amyloplast; here they remain together, although they are easily separated again when the starch is isolated from the tissue. At first the starch granules in the amyloplast are round, but during their growth they touch each other and become angular, remaining separated by narrow layers of stroma (*cf.* Fig. 1-8).[64] The parts of a compound starch granule are sometimes called *granula*. Some of these granula may become fused by a bridge, a phenomenon that has been observed in the alga *Scenedesmus quadricauda,* where complete fusion was achieved under the influence of amitrol.[65] Fusion of starch granules is occasionally observed in other plants as well; the author found examples in chromoplasts of *Aloe* leaves, and in barley endosperm.

The amylose content of rice starch does not change much during

60 Badenhuizen, *Recu. Trav. Bot. Néerl., op. cit.*
61 D. von Wettstein, *Canad. J. Bot.,* **39,** 1537 (1961).
62 J. Veleminsky and G. Röbbelen, *Planta,* **68,** 15 (1966).
63 M. Lefort, *C. R. Acad. Sci. (Paris),* **245,** 437, 718 (1957).
64 M. S. Buttrose, *Naturwiss.,* **49,** 307 (1962).
65 P. Castelfranco and T. Bisalputra, *Amer. J. Bot.,* **52,** 222 (1965).

development within one variety and stays for instance around 20 percent throughout the ripening stage[66] or it may increase from 18 percent to 22 percent during the first three weeks.[67] This may be a consequence of the limited growth of the granula, which do not become much larger than the small granules of wheat, rye or barley starch (4μ- 6μ). However, between rice varieties the range of amylose content varies considerably, namely from 15.5 percent to 37 percent, as does the degree of crystallinity in the starches and the amylose isolated from them.[68]

The function of the glucosyl transferase in the biogenesis of rice starch has been the subject of a series of papers. The compound ADPG has been shown to be a natural constituent that is more efficient than UDPG as a substrate for glucosyl transferase.[69] In all cases the ADPG-glucosyl transferase incorporated glucose into existing starch molecules,[70] and this glucose was added to the nonreducing ends of the chains. Addition of UDP inhibited this incorporation, but UDPG might still be involved in the conversion of sucrose to starch through the sucrose transglucosylase system.[71] The ADPG-glucosyl transferase produced α-1,4, but no α-1,6 glucosidic linkages; oligosaccharides could be lengthened with maltose as the shortest acceptor, but this did not lead to the formation of starch.[72] The transferase enzyme appeared to be stabilized by amylose.[73] Waxy rice starch contained no ADPG-glucosyl transferase, but the enzyme was present in the supernatant.[74] Since this supernatant was obtained by grinding whole rice grains, the transferase might well have been located in the sporophytic tissue, but could have been absent in the endosperm, as in corn.[75]

66 I. Hamada, *Chem. Abstr.*, **61**, 4714 c, e, f (1964).

67 M. Taki, *Chem. Abstr.*, **58**, 2559f (1963).

68 J. C. Lugay and B. O. Juliano, *J. Appl. Polymer Sci.*, **9**, 3775 (1965); and A. C. Reyes, E. L. Albano, V. P. Briones, and B. O. Juliano, *Agric. Food Chem.*, **13**, 438 (1965).

69 T. Murata, T. Minamikawa, and T. Akazawa, *Biochem. Biophys. Res. Commun.*, **13**, 439 (1963).

70 Akazawa, *et al.*, *op. cit.*; and T. Murata and T. Akazawa, *Arch. Biochem. Biophys.*, **114**, 76 (1966).

71 Akazawa *et al.*, *op. cit.*; and T. Murata, T. Sugiyama, T. Minamikawa, and T. Akazawa, *Arch. Biochem. Biophys.*, **113**, 34 (1966).

72 Murata and Akazawa, *op. cit.*

73 T. Akazawa and T. Murata, *Biochem. Biophys. Res. Commun.*, **19**, 21 (1965).

74 Murata and Akazawa, *op. cit.*; and Murata, Sugiyama, and Akazawa, *op. cit.*

75 Akazawa and Nelson, *op. cit.*

Glucose-6-phosphate did not stimulate ADPG-starch glucosyl transferase in rice,[76] in contrast to its effect on a similar enzyme involved in glycogen synthesis. This is one indication that the enzyme systems in plants and animals are not entirely comparable, even if the final products are closely related in chemical structure; and, of course, animals lack plastids.

The work done with rice confirms Leloir's pioneer work,[77] yet it failed to show that ADPG-glucosyl transferase is capable of synthesizing starch *ab initio.* The arguments supporting a synthetic role for the transferase are often difficult to follow. Murata and Akazawa, for instance, draw attention to the fact that maltose is the shortest acceptor for ADPG-glucosyl transferase,[78] while maltotriose is the shortest primer for phosphorylase, although not a very good one.[79] It would follow that only glucosyl transferase can make starch *de novo.* Is it not more logical to assume that oligosaccharides, produced from maltose by means of the transferase enzyme, can act as primers for phosphorylase action with glucose-1-phosphate?

Other workers have stressed the fact that in rice the localization of phosphorylase coincided with that of starch synthesis.[80] The pH of rice endosperm cells ranged from 5.6 to 6.2, which is near the optimum for phosphorylase activity[81] but precludes ADPG-starch glucosyl transferase activity with its optimum at pH 8.4.[82] Phosphate, possibly liberated during the process of starch formation by means of phosphorylase action, did not accumulate in the plastids,[83] and thus an unfavorable ratio of inorganic to organic phosphate is prevented at the site (p. 28). In the earliest stages the endosperm contained much phosphate, accumulated in special bodies in the cytoplasm, but it gradually disappeared from there and was later found mainly in the aleuron layer.[84]

Both phosphorylase (P-enzyme) and branching or Q-enzyme activities increased in rice endosperm during the first two weeks after

[76] Murata, Sugiyama, and Akazawa, *op. cit.*

[77] L. F. Leloir, M. A. Rongine de Fekete, and C. E. Cardini, *J. Biol. Chem.*, **236,** 636 (1961).

[78] Murata and Akazawa, *op. cit.*

[79] D. French and G. M. Wild, *J. Amer. Chem. Soc.*, **75,** 4490 (1953).

[80] R. Aimi and T. Murakami, *Proc. Crop. Sci. Soc. Japan,* **23,** 277 (1955).

[81] R. Aimi and T. Murakami, *Bull. Nat. Inst. Agric. Sci. Japan,* **12** D, 1 (1964).

[82] A. Doi, K. Doi, and Z. Nikuni, *Biochim. Biophys. Acta,* **113,** 312 (1966).

[83] R. Aimi and K. Fujimaki, *Chem. Abstr.*, **58,** 7140 f (1963), and personal communication.

[84] Aimi and Murakami, *op. cit.*

pollination and then decreased sharply, while the amylase activity increased slowly during maturation.[85] The fact that there is little difference in the activities of P- and Q-enzymes among rice varieties, including the waxy variety, is sometimes quoted as evidence against a function of these enzymes in starch synthesis.[86] However, one may well ask, if the phosphorylase system is not involved in the synthesis of waxy starch, and ADPG-glucosyl transferase is absent, how is this starch synthesized? We are inclined to assume that the factors protecting linear molecules from becoming branched are absent in waxy endosperm; since this coincides with the absence of the glucosyl transferase enzyme in the starch granules, the two may be related.

Fatty acids (namely, palmitic, oleic, and linoleic) have been reported to interfere with Q-enzyme activity by forming complexes with amylose, leaving the amylose unavailable as substrate for the Q-enzyme; the waxy endosperms contained only very little of these fatty acids.[87] Complex formation with fatty acids has been known for a long time, and it is assumed that the acids are located inside the amylose helices, in the same way as iodine molecules.[88] Fatty acids may be among those substances in the stroma that are able to influence starch composition.[89]

5-5. DARNEL (LOLIUM TEMULENTUM L.)

The changes in molecular-size distribution of carbohydrates have been followed during the ripening of attached and detached fruits of this poisonous grass species.[90] In general, a shift was found from free sugars, through short-chain cold-water-soluble saccharides, to starch, and this happened more quickly in detached fruits. Phosphorylase was considered to be the enzyme involved in starch synthesis and its action thought to be mainly dependent upon the supply of substrate, although dehydration might have an influence as well.

[85] Hamada, *op. cit.*

[86] Murata and Akazawa, *op. cit.*

[87] Hamada, *op. cit.*

[88] F. F. Mikus, R. M. Hixon, and R. E. Rundle, *J. Amer. Chem. Soc.*, **68**, 1115 (1946).

[89] N. P. Badenhuizen, *Nature*, **197**, 464 (1963).

[90] J. L. Stoddart, *Ann. Bot. N. S.*, **30**, 311 (1966).

5-6. DIEFFENBACHIA *SP.* (SCHOTT.)

This well-known ornamental plant produces elongated starch granules in its stem from chloroamyloplasts,[91] as in *Pellionia* (p. 90); but *Dieffenbachia* starch shows an *A*-spectrum, while *Pellionia* starch has an x-ray diffraction pattern of the *B*-type.[92] After the starches were stained with acridine orange the fluorescence in ultraviolet light was predominantly green for *Pellionia,* and mostly red for *Dieffenbachia,* in agreement with the rule that *A*-starches give a red, and *B*-starches give a green fluorescence color under these circumstances (p. 48). This example emphasizes that it is the genetically controlled composition of the plastidal stroma, rather than the environment provided by an organ (such as a stem) that controls the crystalline pattern of the starch granules.

5-7. TAPIOCA (MANIHOT UTILISSIMA POHL)

The starch from the root tubers of *Manihot* consists of compound granules, each with two granula. This tuber starch has an *A*-spectrum.[93]

The tubers were found to contain a high level of phosphorylase activity,[94] but none could be demonstrated in the isolated starch.[95] During the growth of the tuber the starch content increased, but the activity of the UDPG-glucosyl transferase in the isolated starch dropped after an initial increase.[96] The starch granules showed a high endogenous activity and could produce UDP without the addition of UDPG. They appeared to contain the enzymes and substrates necessary for the addition of glucose residues onto the starch molecules.[97] The possible importance of such processes in relation to the increase of linear material inside the granule by means of intussusception has already been discussed (see p. 69).

91 N. P. Badenhuizen, *Rev. Biol.* (*Lisbon*), **4,** 113 (1964).
92 F. H. Zobel, personal communication.
93 C. Legrand and O. Yovanovitch, *C. R. Acad. Sci.* (*Paris*), **245,** 1553 (1957).
94 P. N. Viswanathan and L. M. Srivastawa, *Indian J. Biochem.,* **1,** 133 (1964).
95 Viswanathan and Krishnan, *op. cit.*
96 *Ibid.*
97 P. N. Viswanathan and P. S. Krishnan, *Indian J. Biochem.,* **2,** 69 (1965).

CHAPTER SIX

B - STARCHES

6-1. POTATO (SOLANUM TUBEROSUM L.)

POTATO STARCH HAS BEEN THE PROTOTYPE OF A B-STARCH EVER SINCE J. R. Katz started his investigations of the x-ray diffraction patterns.[1] In many respects potato starch differs from all other *B*-starches in having exceptionally high hygroscopicity, density, swelling power, and birefringence. In addition its amylopectin contains esterified phosphate,[2] which contributes to the swelling power and the occurrence of strongly negative charges. These negative charges are responsible for the accumulation of the chromogenic cation of acridine orange which causes red fluorescence in ultraviolet light.[3] Nothing is known about the mechanism of phosphate esterification.

The strong birefringence of potato starch indicates better alignment of the molecular chains than in any other starch.[4] Molecular association and distribution seem to be homogeneous in a tangential direction in the potato starch granule. Schoch and coworkers[5] came to the conclusion that the molecules should be laterally linked by weak bonds of approximately uniform strength and that there were no areas of strong micellar organization or random disorganization. They suggested that, in potato starch, the hydrogen bonding occurs as hydrate water bridges rather than by strong direct association. At

[1] J. R. Katz, *Phys. Z.*, **25**, 659 (1924).
[2] M. W. Radomski and M. D. Smith, *Cereal Chem.*, **40**, 31 (1963).
[3] N. P. Badenhuizen, *Stärke*, **17**, 69 (1965).
[4] N. P. Badenhuizen, *Protoplasmalogia*, **2**. B. 2 b δ (1959).
[5] H. W. Leach, L. D. McCowen, and T. J. Schoch, *Cereal Chem.*, **36**, 534 (1959).

the same time, however, there would be many of such hydrogen bonding forces.

Such a compact, hydrated structure of well-oriented molecules explains many of the properties of potato starch. Intensive drying changes the x-ray spectrum of potato starch much more than that of corn and tapioca starch.[6] Amylases cause exocorrosion (p. 53), leaving spindle-shaped residues. Even the smallest residues show undiminished red fluorescence in ultraviolet light with acridine orange: these residues are highly birefringent and are still intact, although the amorphous layers must have become exposed (see Fig. 4-2).[7]

On the basis of this evidence one would expect the stroma of the amyloplasts in the potato tuber to provide for conditions of crystallization in a highly hydrated environment.[8] The stroma might therefore contain a low concentration of proteins in the presence of strongly hydrated ions. The protein content of potato starch is low indeed (0.05 percent), and among the adsorbed ions potassium is prominent. Years ago Zwikker suggested that potassium ions played a role in shaping the constitution of the potato starch granule, and he contrasted this with wheat starch, in which calcium ions were predominant.[9] An analysis of the stroma of amyloplasts is desirable, but it is extremely difficult to obtain sufficient material for biochemical work since most amyloplasts contain starch granules and therefore these plastids can not be isolated in an undamaged condition.

Electron microscope studies indicate that the amyloplasts of the tuber and the fruit of the potato are characterized by accumulations of small osmiophilic particles (Fig. 6-1), which consist of phytoferritin.[10] Prolamellar bodies occur and are the origin of thylakoids when potatoes are exposed to light (Fig. 6-2).[11] In the stroma dense patches develop which become surrounded by a lipid membrane. Their appearance is similar to concentrations of material in the

6 C. Legrand and O. Yovanovitch, *C. R. Acad. Sci.* (*Paris*), **245**, 1553 (1957).

7 Badenhuizen, *Stärke, op. cit.*

8 N. N. Hellman, T. F. Boesch, and E. H. Melvin, *J. Amer. Chem. Soc.*, **74**, 348 (1952).

9 J. J. L. Zwikker, *Recu. Trav. Bot. Néerl.*, **18**, 1 (1921); *Recu. Trav. Chim. Pays-Bas*, **40**, 605 (1921).

10 N. G. Marinos, *J. Ultrastruct. Res.*, **17**, 91 (1967).

11 N. P. Badenhuizen and R. Salema, *Rev. Biol.* (Lisbon), **6**, 139 (1967).

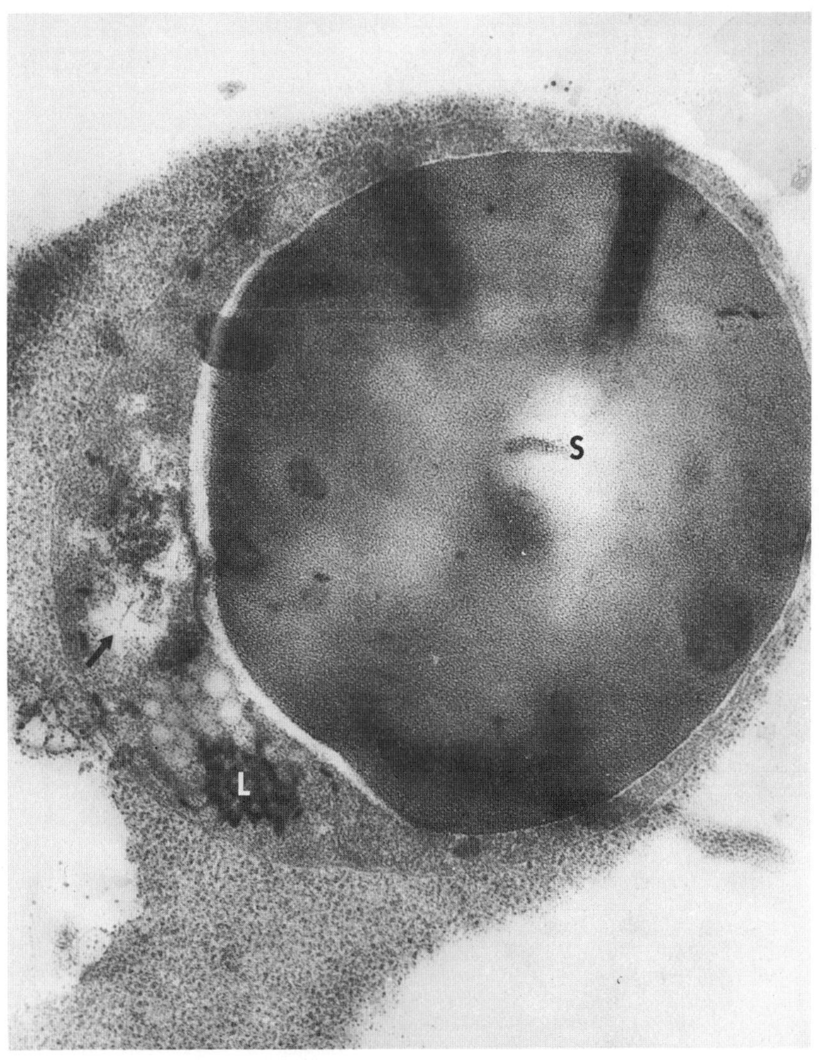

FIG. 6-1. Ultrathin section through part of an amyloplast from a young potato tuber, containing a large starch granule (S). In the stroma a conglomerate of osmiophilic droplets (L) and some DNA fibers (arrow) are visible. Glutaraldehyde–Os fix. Prim. magnif. 20,000 ×. Photo: R. SALEMA.

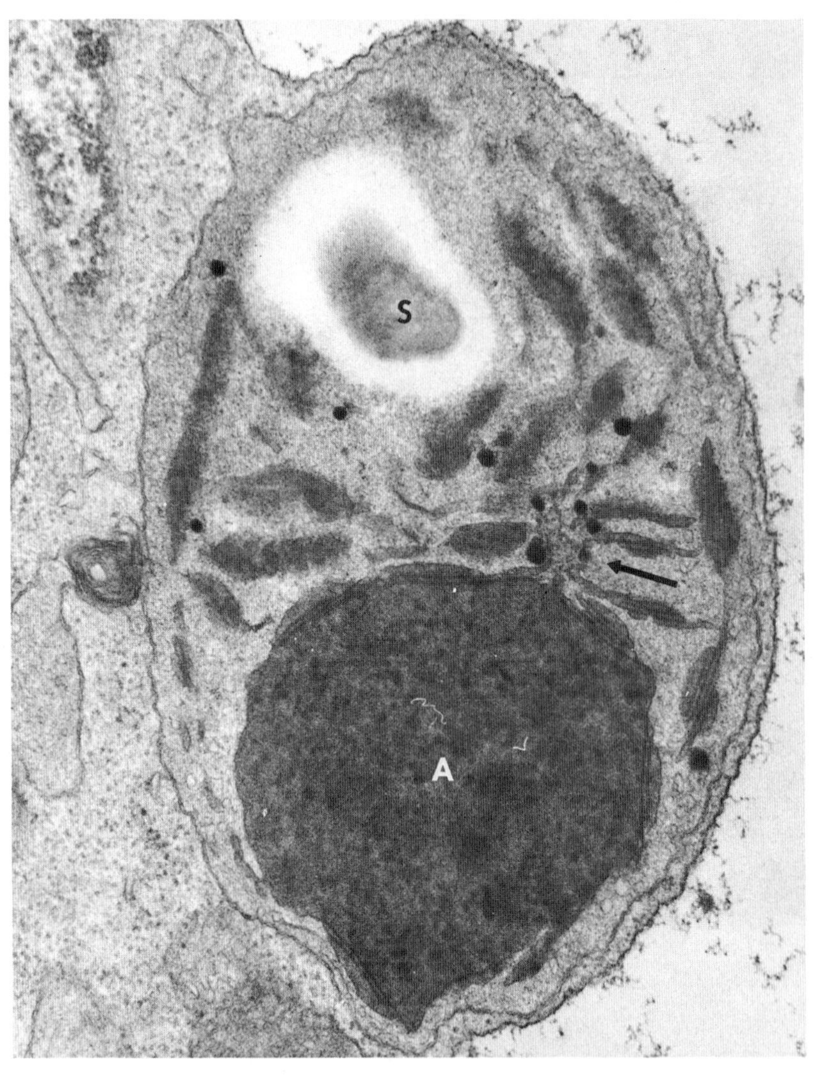

Fig. 6-2. Ultrathin section through an amyloplast from a greening potato. Thylakoids, building up grana, are formed from a prolamellar body (arrow). Most grana are seen in tangential section. Some of them are part of the lipid membranes surrounding a protein body (A) with dense osmiophylic contents. The stroma contains several dispersed globuli and a starch granule (S). Glutaraldehyde and Os fix. Prim. magnif. 7000 ×. Photo: R. Salema.

stroma of chloroamyloplasts of *Pellionia* (see p. 93); however, they also resemble the "intraplastid bodies" described for the plastids in the meristematic cells of potato buds.[12] Such local accumulations or pockets can act as centers for starch crystallization, but this has not been demonstrated as yet for the potato amyloplast. Here, starch granules may originate in the stroma from an accumulation of starch precursors. Similar observations have been made by Hölzl.[13]

The fruit wall of the immature and green berry contains a layer of chlorenchyma. In the peripheral cells of this layer poorly developed chloroplasts are found arranged around the nucleus (see Fig. 1-10). Farther away from the periphery such plastids show a large dense body surrounded by a membrane and similar to the pockets mentioned, but no starch is formed as yet. Only in deeper layers of the cortex do we find the production of compound starch granules. They increase in size, but remain grouped around the nucleus (Fig. 6-3). Finally, in the central pith large, single starch granules, similar to those from the tuber, are found. Their chemical composition is identical to that of the tuber starch,[14] but the layering is much more pronounced and they often show signs of corrosion.

These observations indicate that there are factors in living cells which determine whether a starch granule will be single or compound, and what size it will reach; these factors are a consequence of cell differentiation. Nothing is known about these factors, except that the application of phytohormones has no influence on granule size.[15]

During the development of the starch granules in the growing potato tuber both granule size and amylose content increase while the gelatinization temperature decreases.[16] We can not conclude that amylose percentage and gelatinization temperature are directly related (*cf.* p. 73)—the drop in gelatinization temperature is caused by the large starch granules swelling before the small ones.[17] Therefore, if *size* is accepted as a criterion for maturity,[18] the mature starch granules will be those with the greatest swelling power. In

[12] Marinos, *op. cit.*

[13] J. Hölzl, *Protoplasma,* **60,** 446 (1965).

[14] C. T. Greenwood and S. MacKenzie, *Stärke,* **15,** 251 (1963).

[15] R. T. Whittenberger and G. C. Nutting, *Plant Physiol.,* **24,** 278 (1949).

[16] R. Geddes, C. T. Greenwood, and S. MacKenzie, *Carbohydrate Res.,* **1,** 71 (1965).

[17] N. P. Badenhuizen, *Recu. Trav. Bot. Néerl.,* **35,** 559 (1938).

[18] Geddes *et al., op. cit.*

the potato starch granule, too, there is increasing retrogradation as it grows, but it is not as prominent as in cereal starches.

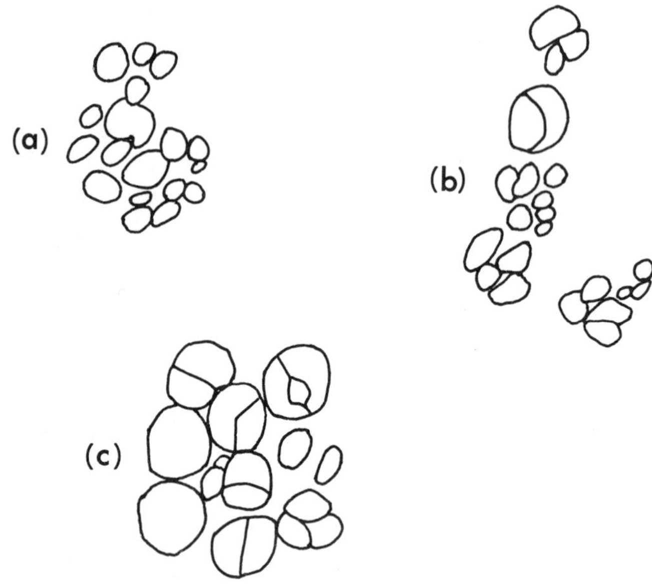

FIG. 6-3. (a), (b), (c). Three stages in the development of compound starch granules from the chloroamyloplasts of Fig. 1-10.

Other interesting observations are the increase of the β-amylase limit and of the limiting viscosity of the amylose during development. The extent to which β-amylase is able to break down amylose molecules depends upon the number of barriers in the linear chain. If these barriers are constituted by branching points,[19] then the increase in β-amylase limit means that the amylose molecules become slightly branched during development. At the same time they increase in length, as indicated by the viscosity data. Amylopectin molecules underwent a slight increase in the degree of branching

[19] W. Banks and C. T. Greenwood, *Arch. Biochem. Biophys.*, **117**, 674 (1966).

and their molecular weight increased.[20] Similar results were found for sweet potato starch:[21] during the development the number of α-1,4 glucosidic linkages increased; this was due to an increase in linear fraction and in average unit chain length of the amylopectin. Not only, therefore, do the starch granules grow, but their molecules grow as well, and both linear and branched fractions become somewhat more branched.

A prolonged action of enzymes included in the starch granule is implied. The observations mentioned above may be taken as evidence for an endogenous activity of ADPG-starch glucosyl transferase. Very little enzyme is necessary for this process, considering the low percentage of protein in potato starch. On the other hand, the enzyme activity is considerable and is dispersed throughout the starch granule since the residues left after exocorrosion (Fig. 6-4) still retain the same activity as the original starch granule.[22]

As in other starches, such as wheat, corn, and rice,[23] a small percentage of an intermediate fraction could be shown.[24]

Corroded residues contain the same amount of amylose, or slightly more, compared to the original granule.[25] This shows that there is a regular overall distribution of amylose and amylopectin throughout the starch granule, although it is not certain that the distribution within one layer would be at random.[26] Since apposition takes place by addition of starch molecules to the periphery of the potato starch granule, we would expect the linear and branched fractions to be intimately mixed and the differences in density between the various parts of a layer to be mainly caused by variation in water content (*cf.* p. 36). On the other hand a process of fractionation can take place whereby molecules of similar chain length crystallize together.[27] This might cause preferential deposition of the longest amylose molecules (p. 90) when a new layer is formed, as has been suggested for potato starch on the basis of microscopic observa-

[20] Geddes *et al., op. cit.*

[21] K. Takahashi, *Agric. Biol. Chem.*, **30**, 629 (1966).

[22] Badenhuizen, *Stärke, op. cit.*

[23] See also A. C. Reyes, E. L. Albano, V. P. Briones, and B. O. Juliano, *Agric. Food Chem.*, **13**, 438 (1965).

[24] Geddes *et al., op. cit.*

[25] Badenhuizen, *Stärke, op. cit.*

[26] N. P. Badenhuizen, *S. Afr. J. Sci.*, **56**, 285 (1960).

[27] P. H. Lindenmeyer, *Science*, **147**, 1256 (1965).

tions.[28] Such a distribution would enhance the difference between the crystalline and the amorphous part of a layer, and consequently the visibility of the layers.

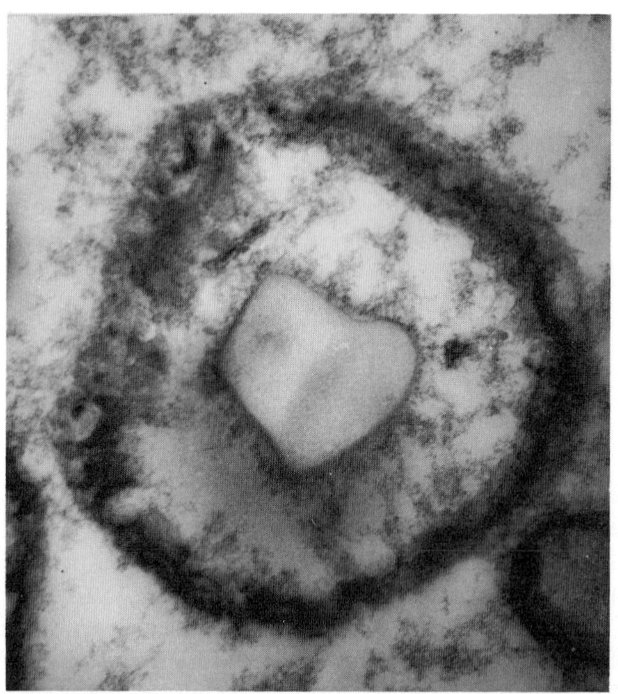

FIG. 6-4. Ultrathin section through a plastid from a germinating potato. The plastid is degenerating and holds a small residue of a corroded starch granule. Note the pseudomembrane around the starch residue. $KMnO_4$ fix. Prim. magnif. 20,000 ×.

A *layer* is defined as an optical section through a three-dimensional shell, as seen under the light microscope. The layers reflect a periodicity in the supply of carbohydrates, so that their density decreases in a centrifugal direction. Long ago Frey-Wyssling indicated that each layer was composed of a number of fine lamellae[29]; these

28 Badenhuizen, *S. Afr. J. Sci., op. cit.*
29 A. Frey-Wyssling, *Protoplasma,* **25**, 261 (1936).

can be made clearly visible under the electron microscope after lintnerization of the starch granules (Fig. 6-5).[30] It should be remem-

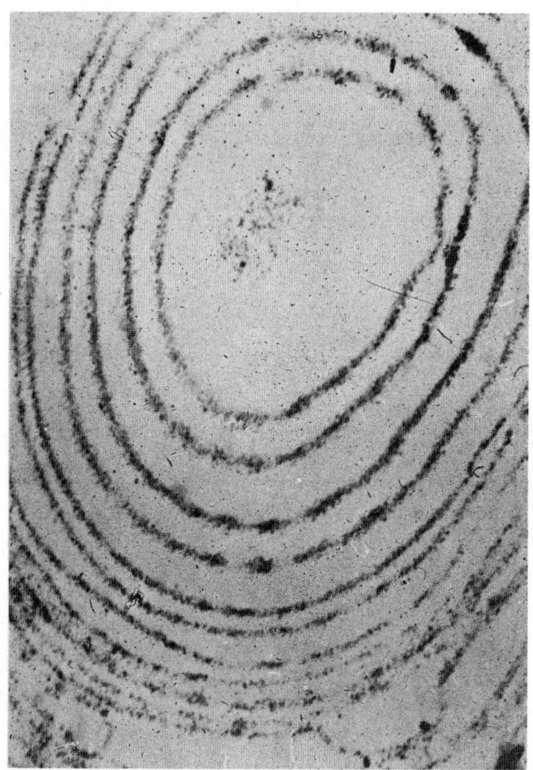

FIG. 6-5. Ultrathin section through the inner part of a lintnerized potato starch granule. The electron microscope reveals many more layers than are visible with the light microscope.

bered that these lamellae are residues left after acid hydrolysis of the more amorphous parts, and thus the measurement of their thickness does not evaluate the original width. In addition amylopectin is preferentially degraded, resulting in an apparent increase in linear material.[31]

[30] A. Frey-Wyssling and M. S. Buttrose, *Makromol. Chem.*, **44-46**, 173 (1961).
[31] J. M. G. Cowie and C. T. Greenwood, *J. Chem. Soc.*, 2658 (1957).

The lamellae of one layer always swell together[32] and groups of layers can swell as a unit.[33] Since each layer or lamella has a greater tangential swelling than the one it surrounds, these will slide past each other, causing a dislocation. Dislocations between lamellae will be invisible, those between layers are clearly visible, while those between groups of layers show a broad dark band under the light microscope.[34] The dark lines are the amorphous parts and may be caused by both a decrease in carbohydrate supply and dislocation as a consequence of slight swelling. This may be the reason that Hess did not always find a decrease in crystallinity from the inside of a layer towards the outside.[35]

That potato starch granules grow by apposition was demonstrated by showing that ^{14}C-labeled carbohydrates produced in the leaves caused a radioactive coating of the granules in the tuber.[36] The fact that some granules showed little radioactivity, indicated that very thin layers could be deposited. The origin of the lamellae may be a consequence of carbohydrate depletion in the immediate vicinity of the starch granule, a further deposit being dependent on diffusion of fresh material from the stroma to the granule. Eventually the stroma is depleted and the molecules deposited are less oriented and more hydrated, thus ending the formation of a layer. A new layer is formed when the amyloplast receives another supply of carbohydrates.[37]

The calculation that one lamella is formed in about two hours[38] probably applies to the diffusion period, rather than to the time necessary for deposition.

Various authors[39] have noted that potato starch granules form layers even under constant conditions, in contrast to what is observed in cereal starches (p. 71). Evidently photosynthetates can reach the endosperm tissue much more quickly than tubers; the result is synchronization of starch deposit with periods of photosynthesis in grass

32 Badenhuizen, *Recu. Trav. Bot. Néerl., op. cit.*

33 Badenhuizen, *Protoplasmologia, op. cit.*

34 Badenhuizen, *Protoplasmologia, ibid.*

35 C. Hess, *Z. Bot.,* **43,** 181 (1955).

36 N. P. Badenhuizen and R. W. Dutton, *Protoplasma,* **47,** 156 (1956).

37 N. P. Badenhuizen, *Protoplasma,* **23,** 440 (1939).

38 A. Frey-Wyssling and K. Mühlethaler, *Ultrastructural Plant Cytology* (Amsterdam, Elsevier, 1965).

39 See, for instance, Hess, *op. cit.*

fruits. In the potato plant other factors, like tuber competition and deficiencies (especially of nitrogen and potassium), influence carbohydrate transport and distribution, which then become independent of the day–night alternation. Layering was also noticed in the granules of small tubers grown on stem pieces under sterile and constant conditions. Since their phosphorylase activity did not fluctuate over twenty-four hour periods, the endogenous rhythm is probably controlled by periodically occurring diffusion gradients as described above.[40]

Both potato starch granules[41] and the juice from potatoes[42] contain ADPG-starch glucosyl transferase. It has been suggested that the biogenesis of the starch granule is dependent on the enlargement of the peripheral amylose and amylopectin molecules by the soluble ADPG-glucosyl transferase or by phosphorylase.[43] This is not supported by electron pictures of growing starch granules (see Figs. 2-1 and 2-2) and does not explain the formation of amylose and amylopectin before the first deposit of starch takes place in the amyloplast. Sandstedt succeeded in growing layers of starch around potato starch granules.[44] Since this was done with the help of phosphorylase, these layers consisted of amylose. They were birefringent, shared the polarization cross with the starch granule inside them, had little swelling power, and were very resistant to the action of amylases. Although the amylose molecules in the artificially produced layers had the same radial orientation as the molecules in the starch granule, there was probably no direct connection between the two, since retrograded starch does not act as a primer for phosphorylase.[45] When the starch granule was made to swell, the rigid new layers were disrupted.

The glucosyl transferase is so much an integral part of the interior structure of the starch granule that the protein can not be washed out, even after the meshes of the paracrystalline network have been widened (p. 37). Adsorption of the enzyme onto the sur-

40 N. P. Badenhuizen and M. J. Malkin, *Nature,* **175,** 1134 (1955).

41 R. B. Frydman and C. E. Cardini, *Biochem. Biophys. Res. Commun.,* **17,** 407 (1964).

42 R. B. Frydman and C. E. Cardini, *J. Biol. Chem.,* **242,** 312 (1967).

43 R. B. Frydman and C. E. Cardini, *Arch. Biochem. Biophys.,* **116,** 9 (1966); and M. A. Rongine de Fekete, *Arch. Biochem. Biophys,* **116,** 368 (1966).

44 R. M. Sandstedt, *Cereal Sci. Today,* **10,** 305 (1965).

45 D. French and G. M. Wild, *J. Amer. Chem. Soc.,* **75,** 4490 (1953).

face of potato starch granules during their isolation could not be demonstrated (p. 35).

When potato tubers were aseptically grown on pieces of stem at various temperatures, the UDPG- (and ADPG-) starch glycosyl transferase activity in the starch granules showed a maximum at 18°C, decreasing to zero at 30°C.[46] Since the percentage of amylose remained the same at all temperatures, it was clear that the enzyme activity, being dependent on external conditions, could show no correlation with the amount of amylose present. Unfortunately, there is, as yet, no other way of measuring the quantity of protein representing glucosyl transferase.

Potato tubers have been a classic source of phosphorylase since the discovery of that enzyme by Hanes, and many other enzymes involved in carbohydrate metabolism have been identified in the tubers. Phosphorylase activity increases with the development of the tuber up to a certain level, then starts to decrease, and finally the enzyme loses its activity during germination, so that most of the starch breakdown is amylolytic.

The amylose chains of potato starch are much longer (DP 3000) than in most starches.[47] Husemann showed that with a continuous supply of glucose–1–phosphate and removal of inorganic phosphate by means of dialysis, very long (DP 10,000) amylose chains could be built up by phosphorylase.[48] If phosphate were removed from the stroma of the plastid, for instance by esterification to the branched starch molecules, the production of amylose chains longer than usual would be promoted.

6-2. PELLIONIA DAVEAUANA N. E. BR.

Pellionia is a creeping plant from tropical Asia and Polynesia, belonging to the Nettle family (*Urticaceae*), although it does not sting. It is widely cultivated in greenhouses, mainly for use by students, who find it easy to study starch formation in the permanently green amyloplasts of the stem of the plant. These chloroamyloplasts

[46] N. P. Badenhuizen and K. R. Chandorkar, *Cereal Chem.*, **42**, 44 (1965).
[47] C. T. Greenwood and J. Thomson, *J. Chem. Soc.*, 222 (1962).
[48] E. Husemann, *Makromol. Chem.*, **35**, 239 (1960).

were first described by Dodel, [49] and later, more critically, by his student Binz.[50] Dodel concluded that the starch granules of *Pellionia* provided the most beautiful example of growth by apposition (Fig. 6-6).

FIG. 6-6. Starch granules in the chloroamyloplasts of a *Pellionia* stem. Appositional growth is directed by the stroma collected at the distal ends of the granules leading to eccentricity of shape. After BINZ (1892).

A transverse section through the stem shows that no starch is present in the chloroplasts of the collenchyma, but starch granules are formed in the cortex, first as small, round granules, which increase in size and become eccentric towards the center of the pith. The large starch granules have the bulk of the plastid attached at the distal end as a green "cap," (Fig. 6-6), but the light microscope can not reveal that the plastidal envelope, consisting of two unit membranes, still surrounds the rest of the granule. Binz already described the grana in the chloroamyloplasts (see Fig. 4-2), and it is the existence of lamellar structures, that keeps the bulk of the stroma together as a cap, and prevents it from becoming evenly distributed around the starch granule.[51] Since starch formation takes place in

49 A. Dodel, *Flora,* **75**, 267 (1892).
50 A. Binz, *Flora,* **76**, 34 (1892).
51 N. P. Badenhuizen, *Proc. Kon. Nederl. Akad. Wetensch.,* **65** C, 123 (1962).

the stroma, the result is a practically one-sided supply of carbohydrate. The granule therefore mainly grows at the distal end, i.e., away from the hilum or point of origin, and consequently it becomes eccentric in shape. Figure 4-2 shows that caps can still be attached to starch granules which are in the process of corrosion.

Binz gives the following description of the development of the starch granules. The initial cells in the vegetation point of *Pellionia* contain leucoplasts, characteristically arranged around the nucleus. At a distance of 230μ from the tip they become green and move away from the nucleus into the cytoplasm. At a distance of 400μ their size is 2.4μ and they begin to form small starch granules, which first stain reddish with iodine solution, but at a later stage of development stain blue (see Fig. 4-2) (*cf.* p. 57).

The youngest internode contains many small starch granules. Strongest growth takes place in the third and fourth internodes. From the sixth internode on, the granules become irregular in shape and show lateral outgrowths, which are taken as evidence in favor of appositional growth (see Fig. 6-6).

In the leaf both normal chloroplasts and chloroamyloplasts occur side by side (p. 20). (For a comparison of the properties of the reserve starches from *Pellionia* and *Dieffenbachia,* in both cases produced in the stem in chloroamyloplasts, see p. 78.)

Although *Pellionia* plants contain much mucilagenous material, which interferes with fixations and reactions, it could be established that the structure of the chloroamyloplasts does not differ fundamentally from that of a normal chloroplast.[52] When these chloroamyloplasts are exposed to light, photosynthesis can take place, as shown by the incorporation of $^{14}CO_2$ or the reduction of tetrazolium blue (p. 10). We may therefore suspect that their location in the plant (inside the stem and on the lower side of the leaf) prevents the chloroplasts from assimilating, so that for starch formation they become dependent on translocated sugars.

This is confirmed by the observation that starch formation and distribution were the same in white etiolated shoots of *Pellionia,* the only difference being the lack of chlorophyll.[53] An exogenous supply of sugars seems to be a condition for the production of large reserve starch granules in plastids. The peripheral chloroplasts of the *Pel-*

52 R. Salema and N. P. Badenhuizen, *J. Ultrastruct. Res.,* **20,** 383 (1967).
53 D. A. McCracken, *M. Sc. Thesis,* University of Toronto (1966).

lionia stem are potentially able to form starch, as is apparent when sections are incubated with a 4 percent glucose solution. Evidently their supply of sugars is insufficient under normal conditions, although other factors, such as enzyme inhibition, may be involved as well (p. 11). Lack of chlorophyll *b*, as found in mutants of *Arabidopsis*[54] and peas,[55] inhibits starch formation in the plastids. The pea mutant did not form starch even when the tissues were incubated with 5 percent glucose solution, but it is not known whether starch-synthesizing enzymes were absent. In the chloroamyloplasts of *Pellionia* the ratio of chlorophyll *a* to *b* was found to be normal, namely, about 3.[56]

When *Pellionia* plants were subjected to various light intensities, the higher rate of photosynthesis in the leaves was reflected by the production of starch in some of the peripheral chloroplasts in the stem, while the average starch granule size increased, as could be expected.[57] Phosphorylase could be demonstrated histochemically in many cells of the stem tissue, while ADPG-starch glucosyl transferase was present in the starch granules.

The proplastids in the stem apex develop thylakoids from vesicles in a way similar to that described for *Cynodon*,[58] until a structure results which is characteristic for chloroplasts. The stroma of the chloroplasts contains many ribosomes, the stroma of the chloroamyloplasts contains fewer (see Fig. 2-2). The ribosomes in the stroma are smaller than those found in the cytoplasm (Fig. 6-7). One wonders whether this may be so because plastidal ribosomes lack a 23 S component and only contain the 16 S component, as suggested for ribosomal RNA from chloroplasts of spinach and other plants.[59]

In the chloroamyloplasts the stroma ribosomes start producing patches of a substance, presumably protein (see Fig. 2-2). As these patches increase in size, they are surrounded by lipid membranes that grow out from the existing lamellar system, which is now in the process of degeneration. Finally there are one or more patches of concentrated material, crowded with particles, and surrounded by

54 G. Röbbelen, *Naturwiss.*, **44**, 288 (1957)
55 F. Müller, *Planta*, **63**, 65 (1964).
56 McCracken, *op. cit.*
57 McCracken, *ibid.*
58 N. P. Badenhuizen, *Port. Acta Biol.*, 8 A, 57 (1964); and Badenhuizen and Salema, *op. cit.*
59 D. Spencer and P. R. Whitfeld, *Arch. Biochem. Biophys.*, **117**, 337 (1966).

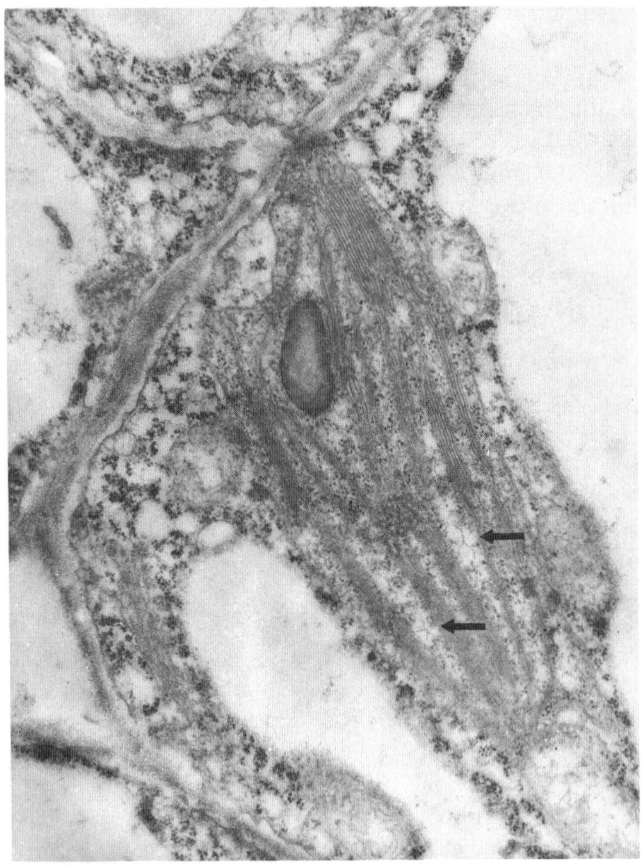

FIG. 6-7. Ultrathin section through a chloroplast from a young leaf of *Pellionia*. In the stroma an assimilatory starch granule, elongated grana, ribosomes and DNA fibers (arrows) are visible. The ribosomes in the stroma are smaller than those in the surrounding cytoplasm. Ryter-Kellenberger fix. Prim. magnif. 20,000 ×. Photo: R. SALEMA.

a lipid membrane (see Fig. 1-11). These structures are the amylogenic pockets; they are visible with the light microscope and contain substances, probably carbohydrates with reducing properties, that stain red with Schiff's reagent. Starch granules crystallize out in the pockets, and during this process the original precursor substance (represented by the particles) and the lipid membranes disappear without leaving a trace. Transitory stages between pockets and starch granule formation have been found, but they are rare so that the crystallization of the first small starch granule must be a very rapid process.[60]

During the subsequent growth of the starch granule its periphery often appears to be fuzzy, and to consist of a particulate material (see Fig. 2-2). Evidently this is the same process, described earlier for the appositional growth of a corn starch granule.[61] One gets the impression that particles of a starch precursor are formed in the stroma until they are so crowded that they become incorporated as a new layer (see p. 65).

Inside the starch granule these particles appear to be strung together in filaments that often show a radial orientation. Not only in ultrathin sections, but also in replicas produced with the freeze-etching technique does one find a particulate structure.[62] When we assume a degree of polymerization of 3000 for potato starch amylose, the corresponding chain length (about 10,000 Å) shows a large discrepancy with the size of the particles (150 Å to 200 Å). The conclusion is inescapable that the molecules are folded many times, as proposed by Mühlethaler.[63] Doubt has been expressed about the probability of such folding,[64] and the events that would bring about folding and orientation in a radial direction are unknown.[65] It has been suggested that the molecules might become oriented under the influence of bivalent cations.[66]

According to Lindenmeyer[67] folding would account for the plasticity of the starch granule in water, while mechanical damage would cause unfolding and make the molecules more accessible to the action of enzymes (*cf.* p. 30). Partial transformation into the more stable extended chain form could take place during crystallization, whereby the conformation with the lowest free energy should be the one that makes the iodine complex possible. The requirement of

60 Salema and Badenhuizen, *op. cit.*
61 Badenhuizen, *Proc. Kon. Nederl. Akad. Wetensch., op. cit.*
62 K. Mühlethaler, *Stärke,* **17**, 245 (1965).
63 Mühlethaler, *ibid.*
64 C. Sterling, *Food Technol.,* **19**, 97 (1965).
65 D. Gallant and N. Crozet, *J. Microsc.,* **5**, 51a (1966).
66 H. Thiele, *Naturwiss.,* **54**, 136 (1967).
67 Lindenmeyer, *op. cit.*

fractionation, whereby similar chain lengths crystallize together, would be more pronounced at greater heterogeneity of molecular size. Lindenmeyer remarks that the formation of such a crystal requires both time and a high degree of molecular mobility. Although we can attempt to make comparisons between artificial and natural spherocrystals, nothing certain is known about the starch granule in this respect.

6-3. LEAF STARCHES

Green leaves contain chloroplasts in the mesophyll, and starch is formed directly by the photosynthetic process. This starch is therefore called *assimilatory starch* and is deposited in the stroma between the thylakoids in the form of tiny granules adapted in shape to the narrow spaces available (Fig. 6-8). The birefringence of these small granules is extremely weak. In the leaves of sunflowers they were found to be simple, concentric, discoid, and 1.2μ to 2.5μ in size.[68] Assimilatory starch is characterized by its metabolic accessibility in an intact chloroplast. Only when the thylakoid structure is broken down, as in maturing tobacco leaves, is the chloroplast transformed into an amyloplast that will deposit larger starch granules of a more permanent nature, that is, reserve starch (p. 15). The leaf starches investigated showed a *B*-spectrum; this may apply to all assimilatory starches.

An exception must be made for the guard cells of the stomata in the leaf epidermis. Their plastids contain the same chlorophylls as found elsewhere in the leaf, but the starch formed in the plastids is reserve starch[69] and is retained in the dark.[70] In broad bean leaves starch appears already in stoma initials, and the submerged flower buds of the water lily have incompletely developed guard cells which contain large starch granules. There seems to be a continuous stream of dissolved materials in the direction of the stomata, causing a physiological polarity which can be made visible by plasmolysis.[71] For that reason chlorophyll may not be as necessary a factor in the

[68] M. A. Radwan and C. R. Stocking, *Amer. J. Bot.*, **44**, 682 (1957).
[69] N. P. Badenhuizen, *Protoplasma*, **62**, 306 (1966).
[70] J. E. Pallas, *Bot. Gaz.*, **125**, 102 (1964).
[71] U. Maercker, *Protoplasma*, **60**, 173 (1965).

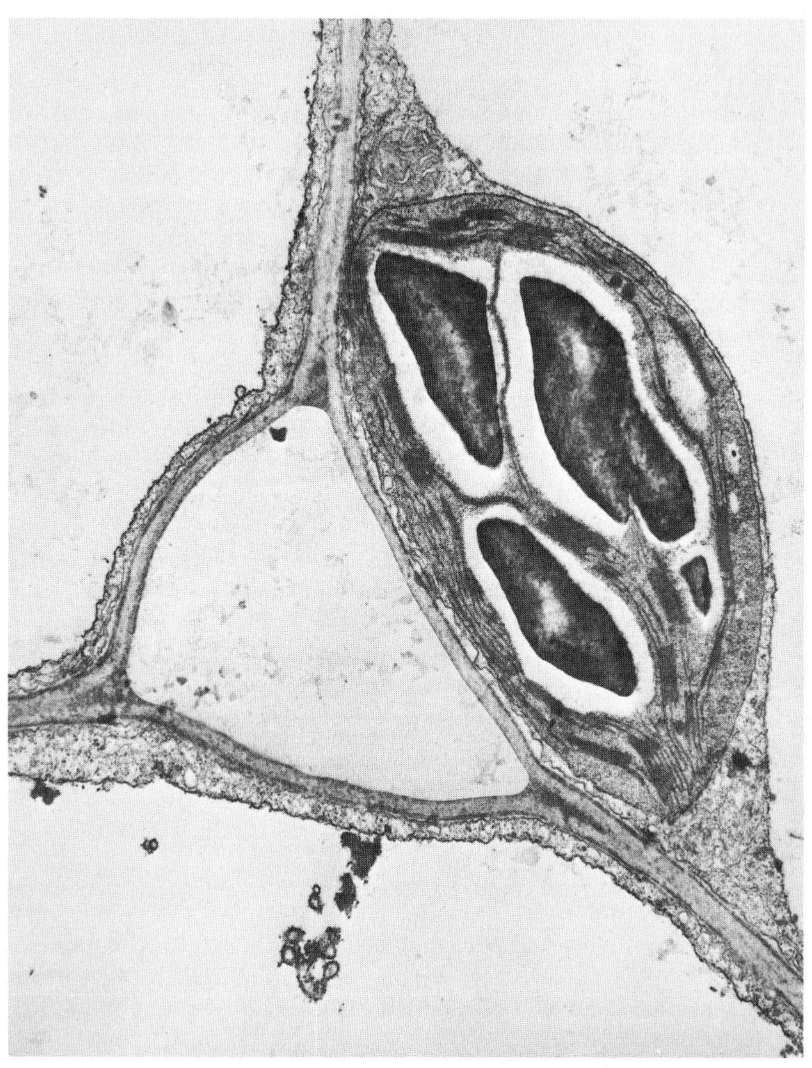

FIG. 6-8. Ultrathin section through a chloroplast from a leaf of Swiss chard, showing assimilatory starch granules, grana and DNA. The shape of the starch granules is controlled by the available space. A wedge-shaped structure, acting as an obstacle, causes one granule to be split. Glutaraldehyde and Os fix. Prim. magnif. 7000 ×. Photo: R. SALEMA.

metabolism of guard cells as was generally thought. This is supported by the observation that the plastids in the guard cells of grasses do not develop beyond the proplastid stage. There is no chlorophyll in what little structure they show and therefore photosynthesis does not take place.[72] Nevertheless these plastids do form starch, and the precursor must therefore come from the surrounding cells.

Starch production may be linked simply to an osmotic effect, since mannitol, which is not metabolically active, can induce starch formation in tissue cultures.[73] Wilting indeed causes an increase in starch content, while during rehydration the reverse process takes place.[74]

In maturing coffee leaves the starch granules in the guard cells are degraded by exocorrosion. They leave vacuoles behind in which fat droplets are produced.[75] However, not all the starch disappears and some may always be available for the sugar-starch conversions, which are regarded as a major factor in the opening and closing of stomata; it is generally thought that phosphorylase is the regulating enzyme. Even in mutants lacking chlorophyll *b,* which characteristically contain no starch, some starch is present in the guard cells.[76]

A number of Monocotyledons, such as the tulip and the snowdrop, do not form starch in their mature leaves. The leaf primordia in the dormant bulbs contain starch, but this disappears as the leaves and flowers develop.[77] Starch formation can be induced by incubation with a glucose solution in all such "sugar" plants (except the onion). Mutants of *Arabidopsis,* lacking chlorophyll *b,* also responded to such treatment.

Wheat, oats, and barley leaves also contain little or no starch. In barley a mutant without cholorphyll *b* was found[78] but there was of course no dramatic difference in starch content with the normal plant. Nevertheless the phosphorylase test was found to be positive in both. When a mutant of *Arabidopsis* without chlorophyll *b* was grown under constant illumination, its leaves showed starch production if they were left overnight in a mixture of chloral hydrate and

72 W. V. Brown and S. C. Johnson, *Amer. J. Bot.,* **49,** 110 (1962).
73 W. Rücker, *C. R. Acad. Sci. (Paris),* **258,** 4826 (1964).
74 J. Deutsch and G. Carlier, *C. R. Acad. Sci. (Paris).* **261,** 2712 (1965).
75 N. P. Badenhuizen. *Protoplasma,* **62,** 306 (1966).
76 Müller, *op. cit.*
77 P. Hagène, *Bull. Soc. Bot. France,* **110,** 73 (1963).
78 H. R. Highkin and A. W. Frenkel, *Plant Physiol.,* **37,** 814 (1962).

iodine, but there was much less starch than in the normal plant. This difference is probably because the chloroplasts in the mutants have an ultrastructure that is much less organized than that of the normal chloroplast,[79] resulting in reduced photosynthetic capacity.

ADPG-starch glucosyl transferase activity has been demonstrated in the chloroplasts of tobacco[80] and spinach,[81] but it is dangerous to generalize from studies performed on one type of plastid only, *in casu* chloroplasts, (p 4). Ghosh and Preiss, for example, concluded that some intermediate of photosynthesis, like 3-phosphoglycerate, may regulate starch synthesis at the ADPG level by its influence on the activity of ADPG-pyrophosphorylase,[82] but this may not apply to amyloplasts, whether colorless or green.

The transferase was also found in starch isolated from bean,[83] tobacco, and *Pelargonium* leaves.[84] The activities of the transferase enzyme were very irregular in starch isolated from tobacco leaves of different physiological ages. Even when the tobacco had been growing under conditions of constant illumination, and all its starch had a constant amylose content of 20 percent, there was still a wide variation in enzyme activity.[85]

Particularly interesting were the results obtained from *Pelargonium* leaf starch. Normally the starch would contain about 21 percent amylose, but when the plants had been destarched during a dark period and then exposed to constant illumination, the amylose content of the newly formed starch had dropped to 11 percent, while its glucosyl transferase activity had also decreased by about 50 percent.[86] Here was another instance (*cf.* p. 33) where a correlation was found between the transferase activity and amylose content.

In explaining these results we should realize that starving a plant in darkness brings about profound changes in the plastids, as the following experiments show. When the chloroplasts of the leaves

[79] D. J. Goodchild, H. R. Highkin, and N. K. Boardman, *Exper. Cell Res.*, **43**, 684 (1966).

[80] Frydman and Cardini, *Biochem. Biophys. Res. Commun., op. cit.*

[81] A. Doi, K. Doi, and Z. Nikuni, *Biochim. Biophys. Acta,* **113**, 312 (1966); and H. P. Ghosh and J. Preiss, *J. Biol. Chem.*, **241**, 4491 (1966).

[82] Ghosh and Preiss, *ibid.*

[83] Badenhuizen and Chandorkar, *op. cit.;* and T. Murata and T. Akazawa, *Biochim. Biophys. Res. Commun.*, **16**, 6 (1964).

[84] Badenhuizen and Chandorkar, *op. cit.*

[85] *Ibid.*

[86] *Ibid.*

of *Beta vulgaris* L. (Swiss chard) had lost their starch after a forty-eight hour dark period, treatment of pieces of leaf in a buffered (pH 6) glucose solution in the light caused the reappearance of starch granules in the intact chloroplasts (see Fig. 6-8). This process could be completely or partially suppressed by the addition of actinomycin D or chloramphenicol to the solution, depending on the concentration of the antibiotic and the duration of its action.[87] Evidently protein synthesis had stopped and the enzymes involved in starch synthesis were not available. As is well-known, actinomycin D blocks DNA and inhibits RNA synthesis without interfering with the RNA already present, whereas chloramphenicol directly inhibits protein synthesis. It had been found before that ADPG-starch glucosyl transferase disappeared during the dark period and was formed again after re-exposure to light; a similar observation was made in respect of phosphorylase.[88] The enzyme activities are clearly correlated with the process of starch formation. It is interesting that the starch which is resynthesized in the light during normal photosynthesis has a much lower amylose content than normal (p. 99), while that produced by incubation in a sugar solution has hardly any amylose at all.[89] Since the glucosyl transferase activity was much lower in such starches, these observations can be taken as evidence for the primary role of phosphorylase in starch synthesis, while the glucosyl transferase might be involved in the steric hindrance of Q-enzyme action (p. 33). Studies of the relative activities of the three enzymes in relation to the composition of the starch produced are desirable (see also p. 106).

The observations discussed above relate to intact chloroplasts. Actinomycin D inhibited RNA production in chloroplasts of anucleated top fragments of the alga *Acetabularia,* but not in the chloroamyloplasts of the basal fragments.[90] These chloroamyloplasts are degenerating chloroplasts and their decreased sensitivity to the antibiotic indicates that RNA and protein production are greatly reduced.

When starch granules in chloroplasts are degraded by amylases during a dark period, we might expect them to release the ADPG-glucosyl transferase they contain. Since no transferase activity was

87 R. Salema and N. P. Badenhuizen, unpublished.
88 K. R. Chandorkar and N. P. Badenhuizen, *Cereal Chem.,* **44,** 27 (1967).
89 K. Doi, A. Doi, and Z. Nikuni, *Stärke,* **18,** 281 (1966).
90 J. Brachet and N. Six, *Planta,* **68,** 225 (1966).

found in the leaf juice after the dark period, the protein had disappeared with the starch.[91] Therefore the enzyme forms an integral part of the structure of the starch granule (p. 37).

ADPG-glucosyl transferase was found in the juice of etiolated bean leaves that had never been exposed to light during germination. Consequently, leucoplasts, amyloplasts, or proplastids may contain starch synthesizing enzymes in the dark, but chloroplasts lose them in the dark, possibly because of the general breakdown of a light dependent system.[92]

Dahlia leaves have been reported to produce assimilatory starch; they contained phosphorylase, but lacked glucosyl-transferase.[93] However, in several instances it has been demonstrated that the properties of a tissue homogenate interfere with enzyme activity. In *Pelargonium,* for instance, the leaf juice had no phosphorylase activity, but it was found that the juice inhibited the enzyme. Many unknown factors can interfere with the enzyme processes of starch production when measured in homogenates.[94]

During the development of a tobacco leaf the chloroplasts become chloroamyloplasts.[95] Starch content increases as does starch granule size, but the starch disappears again in the yellowing leaf. The tobacco leaves may therefore be regarded as temporary storage organs.[96] The reserve starch granules are often compound[97] and show some layering after lintnerization, even if the plants had been growing under constant conditions.[98] This might indicate the existence of an endogenous rhythm; however, under constant conditions the layering was not well defined. In addition, the results of Matheson and Wheatley show a daily periodicity in starch granule growth and iodine affinity (low iodine affinity during the day and a high one during the night), from which they concluded that the metabolism of amylose and amylopectin proceeds at different rates.[99] A high iodine affinity indicates an increase in apparent concentration of

91 Chandorkar and Badenhuizen, *op. cit.*

92 H. Senger and N. I. Bishop, *Plant & Cell Physiol.* (Tokyo), **7**, 441 (1966).

93 P. N. Viswanathan and L. M. Srivastawa, *Indian J. Biochem.,* **1**, 133 (1964).

94 A. Betz, K. Brinkmann and R. Hinrichs, *Planta,* **80**, 77 (1968).

95 N. P. Badenhuizen, *Rev. Biol. (Lisbon),* **4**, 113 (1964)

96 Badenhuizen and Chandorkar, *op. cit.;* and N. K. Matheson and J. M. Wheatley, *Austral. J. Biol. Sci.,* **15**, 445 (1962).

97 See Chapter 5 in Whistler and Paschall, *op. cit.*

98 M. S. Buttrose, *Naturwiss.,* **50**, 450 (1963).

99 N. K. Matheson and J. M. Wheatley, *Austral. J. Biol. Sci.,* **16**, 70 (1963).

linear material, and therefore amylopectin is degraded by preference to amylose during amylolysis at night. Such a pattern of starch degradation agrees with experimental results obtained in other starches (see p. 87).[100] For starch synthesis the situation is different, as amylose and amylopectin are formed simultaneously (see below). The term *metabolism,* as used above, refers to starch breakdown only.

Assuming different rates of amylose and amylopectin production during day and night, Erlander found large discrepancies between theoretical and experimental values, and therefore suggested that both must be produced simultaneously.[101] This also agrees with the growth of a starch granule by particulate apposition, as revealed by the electron microscope (p. 95). Whistler and Young observed that amylose content was not affected by the length of the day,[102] which again tends to show that the rate of amylose production relative to that of amylopectin is the same at night as during the day.

Finally, a biochemical investigation resulted in the suggestion that cellulose and starch have their own specific precursor pools for polysaccharide synthesis within the leaf, and that there is no equilibrium between those pools.[103] The specific relationships between the pools and the polysaccharides they produce is, of course, given by the locations in the cell: the ectoplast for cellulose, the plastid for starch.

6-4. HIGH-AMYLOSE CORN STARCHES

All high-amylose starches have a *B*-spectrum, even if they are found in grasses, which generally contain starch of the *A*-type. In a young stage of development, $aesu_1$ corn showed small starch granules in the endosperm; they contained 20 percent amylose, were round, birefringent, and gave an *A*-spectrum. As they grew they became irregular in shape, nonbirefringent and the spectrum changed to the *B*-type.[104] The original granules were still visible as birefringent nuclei in the optically isotropic mature starch granule,[105] especially

100 See literature in Badenhuizen, *Protoplasmalogia,* 2. B. 2 b δ (1959).
101 S. R. Erlander, *Cereal Chem.,* 37, 81 (1960).
102 R. L. Whistler and J. R. Young, *Cereal Chem.,* 37, 204 (1960).
103 P. Andrews, L. Hough, and J. M. Picken, *Biochem. J.,* 94, 75 (1965).
104 N. P. Badenhuizen, *S. Afr. J. Med. Sci.,* 23, 76 (1958).
105 Badenhuizen, *Protoplasmologia, op. cit.*

after heating in 1.5 percent HCl at 80°C for twenty hours. Sometimes several nuclei were included in a common mass of starch; such granules are semicompound.

After staining with acridine orange some parts of the starch granules showed red, and others green ultraviolet-fluorescence. However, no *A*-pattern could be discerned in the x-ray spectrum of the mature granules. The fact that the bulk of the high amylose granule was nonbirefringent, but showed a sharp *B*-spectrum, means that although crystalline regions were present, they were not arranged in an orderly pattern. The amylose content increased from 20 percent to 66 percent. Long irregularly folded linear molecules may cause deviations from the radial arrangement.[106]

Starting on the sixteenth day after pollination, the amylose content of one high amylose corn variety increased during a fourteen day period of development from 17 percent to 55 percent, that of another similar variety from 25 percent to 52 percent. The second variety grew more quickly, and therefore its amylose content was at a higher initial level than that of the first variety.[107] UDPG-starch glucosyl transferase showed a corresponding increase of activity over the same period of 93 percent and 77 percent respectively for the two varieties. This was one of the few cases where the relationship between the amylose content and the glucosyl transferase activity was directly proportional (p. 99).

In the $aesu_1$ starch described above there is a sudden change from birefringence to optical isotropy. If subsequent layers with increasing amylose content were laid down around the original birefringent granule, we would expect a gradual fading out of the birefringence towards the periphery, assuming that a higher amylose content would be responsible for progressive disorientation of the crystalline regions.[108] Since this is not the case, it is more likely that a sudden change takes place in the enzymatic mechanism of the plastid, causing the production of high amylose starch with a fixed final percentage of amylose in all its layers (p. 69). On high amylose starches do not show birefringent nuclei and their granules may be thread-like structures;[109] they have a *B*-spectrum from the very beginning.

106 *Ibid.*

107 Badenhuizen and Chandorkar, *op. cit.*

108 Badenhuizen, *Protoplasmalogia, op. cit.*

109 Sandstedt, *op. cit.*

High amylose starches have a low swelling power, but the introduction of the gene su_2 depresses the gelatinization temperature, as measured by the birefringence end point method (BEP).[110] For instance, the gene *du*, by itself, induced an amylose content of 41 percent and a BEP of 69°C, whereas the combination *du* su_2, with an even higher amylose content of 50 percent, had a BEP of only 56.5°C. One of the functions of the gene su_2 may be to make more free water available in the plastid and promote hydration of the starch molecules as they become arranged in an orderly pattern in the granule.

6-5. LEGUMINOSAE

Most of the work on starch granule development has been done with the reserve starch of peas and beans; x-ray spectra of these starches vary from *B* to *C*.

In pea cotyledons the starch granules are formed in chloroamyloplasts. The thylakoid structures (grana and intergrana lamellae) become arrayed along the plastidal envelope and in strands traversing the stroma; the granules crystallize out in the spaces left between these strands (see Fig. 1-12).[111] A detailed study of the cotyledons was made by Bain and Mercer.[112] The plastids had a poorly developed structure in the earliest stages of development (the tenth day after fertilization). Nine days later they contained a small starch granule, and from then on the synthesis of starch, fat, and proteins was rapid. Starch granules continued to grow until the forty-fifth day after fertilization, but long before that day they filled up the plastid, in which by this time neither stroma nor lamellae could be seen. The final stages of growth of the starch granule were connected with a sharp drop in the sucrose content (from the twenty-eighth day after fertilization), the sucrose probably being located in the vacuole. It was observed that the intact plastid membranous envelope was never in contact with the starch granule. The authors concluded that the double membrane of the plastid is concerned with the transport of precursors into the plastid and that the final steps in synthesis are

110 **P. L. Pfahler, H. H. Kramer, and R. L. Whistler,** *Science,* **125,** 441 (1957).
111 Badenhuizen, *Rev. Biol.* (*Lisbon*), *op. cit.*
112 J. M. Bain and F. V. Mercer, *Austral. J. Biol. Sci.,* **19,** 49, 69 (1966).

located at the starch-stroma interface. The observations of Badenhuizen substantiate these suggestions of Bain and Mercer (p. 36).

At the end of the ripening period the plastid membrane tends to disappear, so that the starch granule in the germinating seed is exposed to enzymes in the cytoplasm. However, even if the envelope occasionally remains intact, corrosion will proceed in the usual way.[113]

As a rule the reserve starch of *Leguminosae* is found in the cotyledons of the seeds, and its amylose content is relatively high (about 35 percent), that of wrinkled pea starch being 66 percent or higher, depending upon the variety.[114] In exceptional cases, for instance in the tuberous roots of *Phaseolus coccineus* L., there are additional storage organs, and the starch granules in these differ greatly in shape from those in the seeds. The starch in the tubers of *Phaseolus coccineus* consists of tapioca-like granules with an average size of 10 μ to 12 μ, and an amylose content of 27 percent.[115] It follows that the effect of genetic control of starch granule type is modified by cell differentiation. The genes involved in starch formation have a different expression in different reserve organs of the same plant.

The seed starches of many species of *Leguminosae* have been described recently.[116] Most species contained the type of starch granule which is characteristic for bean starch, and the only difference found between them was in size distribution. Few genera had starch granules which deviated from the standard shape.

During the development of pea seeds (both smooth and wrinkled) an increase takes place in starch content, granule size, gelatinization temperature, amylose percentage, and the number of barriers against complete hydrolysis by β-amylase.[117] The barriers which set a limit to beta-amylolysis are probably caused by branching points (p. 84); this would indicate an aftereffect of the Q-enzyme included in the starch granule, causing slight branching of the amylose molecules. The size of the amylose molecules increases during maturation,[118] perhaps as a consequence of endogenous activity of starch glucosyl transferase and phosphorylase (p. 78).

113 Chandorkar and Badenhuizen, *op. cit.*
114 Badenhuizen, *Protoplasmalogia, op. cit.*
115 J. Seidemann and W. Schliepe, *Biol. Zbl.*, **82**, 727 (1963).
116 M. Wellendorf, Bot. T., **62**, 50 (1966).
117 C. T. Greenwood and J. Thomson, *Biochem. J.*, **82**, 156 (1962).
118 *Ibid.*

In peas, as in other plants, sugars are transported in the form of sucrose, and this sucrose is the main material used for starch formation.[119] Sucrose content increased until twenty-five to twenty-eight days after flowering, when both phosphorylase activity and starch synthesis increased rapidly, causing a drop in the sucrose level. This evidence indicates a major role of phosphorylase in starch synthesis. After twenty-seven days much phosphorylase was still present but lack of substrate slowed down starch synthesis (see also p. 100).

The starch granules of wrinkled peas have been described as compound.[120] The impression of a compound granule is created because the mature starch granule is subdivided into segments by radial fissures. By definition a compound starch granule is formed from several granules, originating in one amyloplast and growing together, as in oats (see Fig. 1-8). When an amyloplast only produces one granule, the latter is a simple one. Each amyloplast in a cotyledon of a wrinkled pea produces only one starch granule in which fissures gradually develop. Therefore this starch granule is simple and its similarity to a compound granule is only superficial.[121] Some types of wrinkled pea display a very irregular system of fissures.

In the F_1 generation between smooth and wrinkled peas, starch granules are produced whose tendency to form fissures is greatly reduced; the F_1 starch is in this respect intermediary between that of the parents. Such hybrid starches have also been reported from a cross between two *Hedychium* species (ginger family) and are a striking example of the genetic control of starch granule shape.

Wrinkled-pea starch contains more protein than the starch of smooth peas, and its ADPG-starch glucosyl transferase activity is also considerably higher.[122] It is possible that the increased enzyme activity is related to the high amylose content of wrinkled-pea starch.

The adsorption of phosphorylase to the starch granules of *Vicia faba* L. (broad bean) has been investigated recently.[123] Amyloplasts and starch granules were confused in this article, but this error does

[119] Bain and Mercer, *op. cit.* and D. H. Turner and J. F. Turner, *Austral. J. Biol. Sci.*, **10**, 302 (1957).

[120] For instance, see E. T. Reichert, *Carnegie Inst. Publ.*, **173**, (1913).

[121] Chandorkar and Badenhuizen, *op. cit.;* C. Griebel, *Z. Lebensm. Unters. Forsch.*, **89**, 404 (1949); and H. Kappert, *Z. indukt. Abstamm. Vererb. lehre,* **13,** 1 (1915).

[122] Chandorkar and Badenhuizen, *op. cit.*

[123] M. A. Rongine de Fekete, *op. cit.*

not subtract from the interesting results. The composition and pH of the medium determined whether adsorption took place or not. The optimum pH was found to be in the range 6.3 to 8.0; EDTA promoted adsorption, but sucrose and other sugars inhibited it. This may explain why some investigtors[124] found a high phosphorylase activity in potato starch, whereas others found none. It is possible that the adsorption of other proteins[125] is equally regulated by the composition of the stroma. The conditions in the stroma may vary locally. Adsorption of proteins to part of a starch granule would cover the part with a "pseudo-membrane" (see Fig. 6-4),[126] and prevent its growth on that side. The presence of sucrose near other parts of the granule could cause phosphorylase to move into the stroma, where the enzyme would be active in starch production. The electron pictures show that this happens in the form of coacervate droplets, visible as particles which become incorporated into the periphery of the granule (p. 95, also see Fig. 2-1), and not by the elongation of peripheral molecules.

In soybeans starch is present until fifty-two days after flowering —one week before maturity.[127] The influence of various temperatures on the x-ray spectrum of this starch, as it develops in the seedlings, was as follows: Below 13.5°C a *B*-spectrum, at 16°C a *B*-like *C*-spectrum, at 22°C a *C*-spectrum intermediate between *A* and *B,* and above 28°C an *A*-like *C*-spectrum. If the temperature varied between 13.5°C and 32°C the intermediate *C*-spectrum appearing at 22°C resulted.[128] Such an influence of external conditions may be responsible for the fact that pea starch has sometimes been accredited with a *B*-spectrum, and sometimes with a *C*-spectrum. However, the tendency in leguminous starch is towards the *C*-spectrum, and a higher temperature seems to promote closer molecular association (p. 48).

124 P. K. Pottinger, *Ph. D. Thesis,* University of Western Australia (1964).

125 K. R. Chandorkar and N. P. Badenhuizen, *Stärke,* **18,** 91 (1966).

126 Badenhuizen, *Proc. Kon. Nederl. Akad. Wetensch., op. cit.;* and F. M. Gerola, F. Cristofori, and G. Dassu, *Caryologia,* **13,** 164 (1960).

127 R. F. Bils and R. W. Howell, *Crop Sci.,* **3,** 304 (1963).

128 S. Hizukuri, M. Fujii, and Z. Nikuni, *Nature,* **192,** 239 (1961).

CHAPTER SEVEN

SUMMARY AND CONCLUSIONS

THE TWO FUNDAMENTAL QUESTIONS TO BE ASKED IN THE FIELD OF starch biogenesis are the following: (1) What are the factors influencing the shape of reserve starch granules, so that they become characteristic for a plant species? and (2) What is the mechanism responsible for the presence of linear molecules (amylose) in most starches?

Starch can be formed in all types of plastids, but in those plastids which are connected with an active photosynthetic apparatus the starch granules have no characteristic shape, and are modeled according to the space available. Only the reserve starch granules, produced in amyloplasts, present a genetic problem.

The many factors that can influence starch granule formation are found in the stroma of the plastids. The stroma has morphological features which can be recognized under the electron microscope and which are again typical for a plant species. Such morphological features are evidently under genetic control, and this will probably apply to the chemical composition of the stroma as well. If the composition of the stroma is regulated by the action of the plastid membranes, which also may have a hereditary fixed structure, then the study of membrane activities becomes fundamental to our understanding of starch biogenesis.

Chloroplasts contain DNA, but this seems to be connected with the photosensitive system in these specialized plastids, and starch formation is dependent on this system. For leucoamyloplasts or chloroamyloplasts that operate in the dark, the situation is different: they depend on an external carbohydrate supply for starch formation.

A genetically controlled membrane structure regulating the influx of substances that give the stroma its particular composition in the amyloplast, will be perpetuated by plastid division. Leucoplasts also contain a DNA and RNA, which may be responsible for the production of enzymes like phosphorylase. As far as is known variations in shape and composition of reserve starch granules are controlled by nuclear genes, as modified by cell differentiation in the reserve organ concerned.

Division of plastids does not preclude an origin *de novo* and various mechanisms have been suggested for the latter. The electron microscope has not given conclusive evidence for or against such an origin. In the opinion of the author an origin *de novo* does not necessarily contradict the concept of genetic continuity: therefore, continuous research in this problem is desirable.

Amyloplasts and etiolated chloroplasts contain the starch-synthesizing mechanism, but chloroplasts appear to lose it after a prolonged period of darkness. The reappearance of the activity of starch-synthesizing enzymes in chloroplasts after re-exposure to light can be prevented with actinomycin D and chloramphenicol, so that these enzymes are produced by the chloroplasts themselves. Chloroplasts are highly specialized plastids, differing in many respects from amyloplasts. For that reason one should be careful not to make generalizations about starch biogenesis from the study of chloroplasts alone. However, their proplastids may temporarily act as amyloplasts, and chloroplasts can be transformed into chloroamyloplasts. Both proplastids and chloroamyloplasts contain DNA, but the chloroamyloplasts have lost much of their sensitivity to actinomycin D. In other words, they have a greatly reduced protein turnover, which is visibly expressed in a diminished number of ribosomes, as compared to chloroplasts.

In any genetic system the proteins are of paramount importance. The study of protein-carbohydrate complexes will therefore be a fundamental aspect of further progress in the field of starch biogenesis. The presence of certain proteins, initiated by nuclear genes, is likely to influence the way in which starch molecules are formed and assembled. In turn, these proteins are modified in their action by smaller molecules like salts and sugars. Together they provide the physico-chemical environment in the stroma which will determine the production of a certain type of starch granule. They set the stage, as it were, for the crystallization of the final product, a mechanical process. After the deposition of starch in solid form no turnover takes place, although some enzymatic processes may continue for a while inside the granule.

A few proteins seem to have special significance because they are thought to be involved in starch synthesis, namely, the enzymes phosphorylase and ADPG-alpha-glucan glucosyl transferase. A simplified scheme of pathways leading to starch production, based on the evidence discussed in this book, is given in Figure 7-1.

All plastids contain phosphorylase, whether they produce starch under natural conditions or not. The enzyme activity may be suppressed by the presence of amylases or by the lack of G—1—P. Both phosphorylase and starch are found in the stroma, which has the right pH (about 6) for the reaction. During the reaction linear amylose molecules are produced and phosphate is liberated. This phosphate does not accumulate in the plastids but may be stored elsewhere in the cell. Consequently the ratio inorganic/organic phosphate is probably favorable for synthesis at the site of starch formation; in contrast, high ratios are only found in homogenates. A branching (Q) enzyme is also present in the stroma and is able to make amylopectin out of amylose. Somehow a genetically fixed quantity of amylose molecules escape branching. The primers (chains of the maltose series) necessary for the initiation of the phosphorylase reaction are always present in the stroma. Since they can have a considerable influence on the length of starch chains formed, a survey of primers in various plants is desirable.

Biochemical evidence tends to show that first amylose is produced and then amylopectin, and that this takes place outside the starch granule, in the stroma of the amyloplast. This is in agreement with electron pictures revealing that appositional growth takes place by the addition of particulate material, formed in the stroma, to the periphery of the starch granule, but it raises difficult questions such as whether the molecules are folded and in what way a radial orientation is acquired.

Depending on pH and sugar concentration the phosphorylase (and possibly other proteins) can be adsorbed to the granule surface or liberated into the stroma. The conditions may vary at different

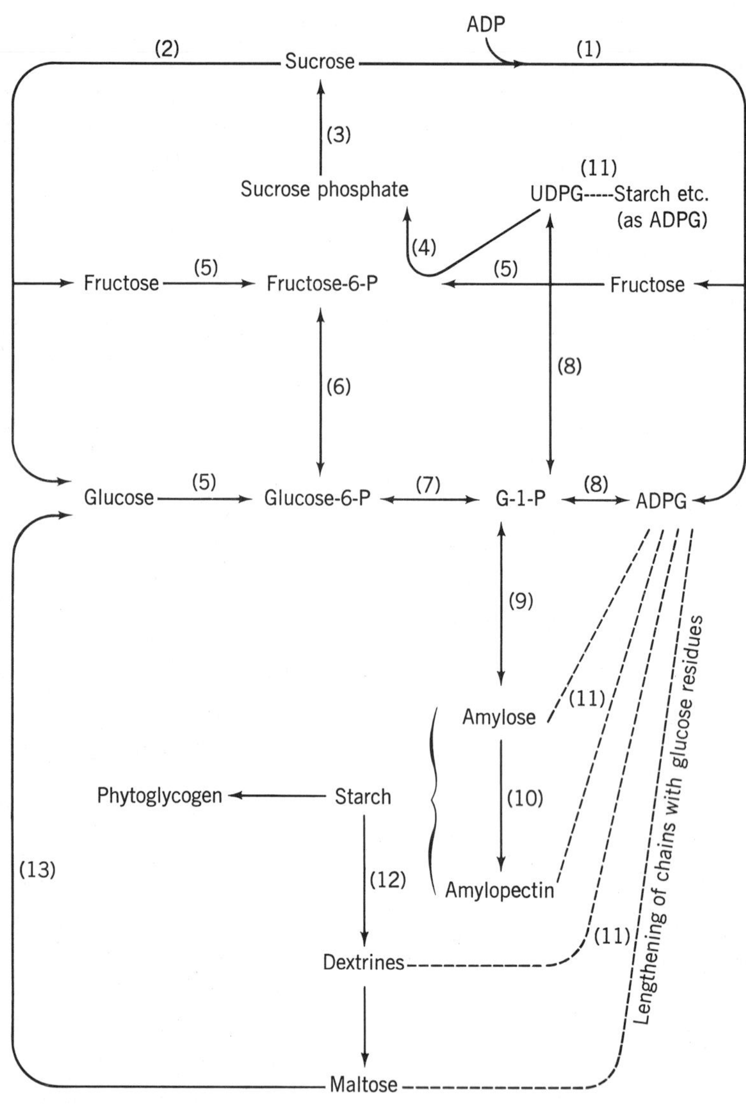

FIG. 7-1. Pathways of carbohydrate metabolism in relation to starch formation with the following enzymes: (1) ADPG-fructose glucosyl transferase, (2) invertase, (3) sucrose phosphatase, (4) UDPG-fructose phosphate glucosyl transferase, (5) hexokinase, (6) isomerase, (7) glucomutase, (8) pyrophosphorylase, (9) phosphorylase, (10) Q-enzyme, (11) α-glucan glucosyl transferase, (12) amylases, (13) maltase.

parts of the granule surface. In case of adsorption a pseudo-membrane covers the surface and at that spot no growth takes place. The phosphorylase, free in the stroma, can participate in the formation of starch molecules, which become highly concentrated, possibly in the form of coacervates. It has been suggested that the multiple production of coacervate droplets, after the usual fixation methods, becomes visible under the electron microscope as a granular material.

Phosphorylase is the only enzyme that is able to make starch *in vitro,* and it is always found in connection with starch-producing tissues. In the opinion of the author no evidence has been presented that would justify the rejection of phosphorylase as a major starch-synthesizing enzyme in living cells of higher plants, and recent investigations support this view. It should be noted that the combined action of the P- and Q-enzymes is insufficient in itself to explain the presence of amylose in starch.

ADPG-glucosyl transferase has the following properties. It is unable to make starch *ab initio,* but can lengthen existing chains with α-1,4 glucosidic linkages, whether they have a low or a high degree of polymerization. Maltose represents the smallest acceptor molecule, and from it the enzyme is capable of producing oligosaccharides that could act as primers for the phosphorylase reaction. Since the transferase is found in amylose-containing starches, but not in waxy varieties, there is a connection with the production of the linear fraction. It is present in soluble form in the stroma and in insoluble form inside the starch granule, where it forms an integral part of the structure. Its dispersion throughout the granule is a regular one, as follows from the activities found in residues of corroded potato starch granules. The enzyme is probably included in the granule during the processes of crystallization and apposition, because it has a strong affinity for starch molecules. This affinity may be instrumental in preventing a number of amylose molecules, formed by phosphorylase, from becoming branched, a view that provides for a link with genetic control. It presupposes that a relationship between the transferase and the amount of amylose exists.

The activity of the ADPG-glucosyl transferase is dependent on various factors, such as temperature, physiological age, and genotype, and in general no correlation has been found between transferase activity and amylose content. However, in a few cases a fair proportionality between the quantity of amylose and the enzyme activity could be established for the starch in one particular tissue during its development or under varying external conditions. Even so, protein content and enzyme activity in the starch granules is of less importance than that in the stroma, where the site of action is.

In general the pH of plastids would be unfavorable for the action of ADPG-glucosyl transferase (optimum pH 8.4). Nevertheless some slow endogenous activity of the enzyme, possibly together with phosphorylase, may go on inside the starch granule. This aftereffect could be responsible for the increase in apparent linear material during the growth of the starch granule. This theory is supported by the increase in chain length observed in developing starch granules of peas and potatoes. Small quantities of the enzymes may be involved in the production of "blue-staining" cores in waxy starch granules.

If amylose and amylopectin are formed simultaneously in the coacervate droplets, mentioned above, they should have a regular distribution throughout the starch granule. Such distribution is apparent from the fact that residues of corroded potato starch granules contain the same amount of amylose as is found in the original granules. Moreover, under constant conditions the addition of material to the growing starch granules in wheat or barley endosperm goes on without interruption, and the resulting nonlayered granules have the same amylose content as the normal ones with layers.

It is plausible that all layers in the mature starch granule have the same composition of mixed amylose–amylopectin crystallites. No convincing evidence has been put forward that shows that there is either more amylose or less amylose in the center of the granule than at the periphery. The swelling phenomena observed in starch granules can be satisfactorily explained on the basis of tangential swelling of layers of equal composition.

In the amyloplasts of corn endosperm starch granules are formed free in the stroma, but also often by preference in pockets created by accumulations of lipid material. Prior to the appearance of starch granules, the stroma, or part of it in a pocket, becomes filled with a dense granular substance which disappears when crystallization takes place. It is therefore suggested that this granular substance consists of starch precursors. In *Pellionia* chloroamyloplasts these pockets have their origin in proteins produced by ribosomes. Patches of this material become surrounded by lipid membranes, grown out from the thylakoids, and finally appear as a dense conglomerate of proteins, and particles which can be removed by treatment with α-amylase. With the crystallization of the starch granule, a rapid process, all traces of the amylogenic pockets disappear. Evidently there is variation in the structures inside the plastids which are involved in starch formation, but the accumulation of precursors is common to all.

Biochemical research, combined with electron microscope observations, is providing an approach to the problem of starch biogenesis. It will not be easy to trace the differences in the minute structures described that lead to the diversification in starch granules. The variability is so great that it is hardly feasible to devise a system of classification. One based on the x-ray diffraction patterns is the most practical one. The properties of starch granules are known at the light microscope level, and their general chemistry has been elucidated. The task ahead is much more difficult and can only be accomplished by studying the processes in the living plastids and by setting up model experiments that imitate them. Some of the problems involved have been outlined in the preceding pages; the solutions of these problems requires cooperation between various disciplines.

INDEX